PATHWAY
to
PRESENCE

The Trager® Approach
as a
Way of Living

AUDREY MAIRI

Author of TRAGER *for* SELF HEALING:
A Practical Guide for Living in the Present Moment

The Presence and Light Company

Canadian Cataloguing in Publication Data

Mairi, Audrey
     Pathway to Presence

ISBN 978-0-9865157-4-3

Copyright © 2011 by Audrey Mairi

Published by AwareNow Publishing, www.awarenow.ca, 2011

Edited by Paul Latour

Line editors: Susan Healey, Jill Kirby and Jean Hopkins

Text design, typography by Paul Latour

Cover design by Paul Latour and Audrey Mairi

Printed by First Choice Books, Victoria, BC

The terms *Trager* and *Mentastics* are trademarked, registered service marks of Trager International.

Also by Audrey Mairi:
Trager for Self-Healing:
A Practical Guide for Living in the Present Moment
published by HJ Kramer/New World Library Publishers
www.newworldlibrary.com

Courses by Audrey Mairi:

The Power of Presence

Trager Introductory Workshop

One day Mentastics Workshop

Six Simple Steps to the Now

See her website at www.audreymairi.com for more information on the above courses and upcoming schedule.

This book is lovingly dedicated to my two wonderful sons, Jeremy and Mischa, who grew up with the constant reminder to, "Pause, breathe, feel your feet, and put in your tail."

"Lift up the self by the Self

And don't let the self droop down,

For the Self is the self's only friend

And the self is the Self's only foe."

Bhagavad Gita [1]

CONTENTS

MENTASTICS CONTENTS

CHAPTER ONE

The Path

At times I feel like a character in an adventure novel, passing through thick forests full of hidden monsters, capturing the flag of a new kingdom, falling into the pits of despair, tearing my hair out with boredom, trekking across the mists into the unknown, landing in a gold mine...

Life is a journey with highs and lows and plateaus. Most of the suffering we experience is created through the stories we tell ourselves along the way. Eating a bowl of cereal does not create suffering in you, but thinking about how your boss keeps passing you over for a promotion *while* you are eating will.

What gives me a measure of grace along my journey is *Presence*—allowing my body and mind to be here in the *Now*. In the *Now*, I can find hidden treasures even in the most difficult situations: the smell of ozone during a thunder storm, meeting a new friend who comes to the rescue when you have a flat tire, the bonding that occurs when a neighbor helps shovel a roof overloaded with snow.

What guides me into the *Now* are specific tools I learned from the principles of the *Trager®* Approach. Since learning them, I have stretched and molded these tools into a form that will bring anyone into the *present moment*, no matter where they are or what is happening in their life.

Traditionally, the *Trager* Approach is considered a kind of bodywork that re-educates a client's movement. In truth, it is much more than that. The premise upon which *Trager* has been built can be used as an effective approach to living. For me, it is responsible for altering my posture, for increasing my emotional intelligence, skyrocketing my empowerment, releasing my anxieties, and consciously connecting me with the underlying intelligence that is all around us.

Trager Psychophysical Integration, as the *Trager* Approach is formally known, was developed by Dr. Milton Trager, a man far ahead of his time, a man who has been called an American Zen Master. He was so attuned to his internal rhythm and feelings that he naturally connected spiritual consciousness with empirical science at a time when the idea of a body/mind connection to Spirit was virtually unheard of in the scientific world. Many devoted people followed him around to soak up his teachings and eventually formed what was then called the *Trager* Institute. That early organization has now been transformed into *Trager* International[1].

---

[1] See appendix for more information on the Trager organization.

Despite *Trager* having organizations in a dozen different countries, the wealth of insights available from this modality remain relatively unknown to the general population. As a cutting edge somatic (of, or relating to, the body) model it remains on the outskirts of awareness for the average seeker.

The aim of this book and CD audio tracks is to concisely (and affordably) show how the principles of the *Trager* Approach can bring a person into *Presence*.

These pages will not teach you how to be a practitioner. The *Trager* organization has highly skilled instructors and a constantly evolving program to do that. Instead, this book will explore what I see as the underlying ideas upon which the work is based and how everyday people can apply them to everyday living. By understanding and using these principles you will gain insight into the power of *Trager* and how it can transform your life.

Over my many years of experience I have distilled the teachings of Dr. Milton Trager into a series of deceptively simple tools. Through them you will learn to *Hook-Up* or connect to a *present moment* awareness, to increase your emotional intelligence, work with the body/mind connection, and somatically align yourself with the powerful and intelligent flow from which we are made and by which we are surrounded.

From these simple tools you will learn to "unstick" yourself from your projections of the past and future. You will find insecurity, poor health, depression, and instability slipping away like snow melting under a hot sun.

Our world is changing faster than ever before. No longer can we take anything for granted. No longer can we expect our lives to grow as they have in the past. New strains of viruses threaten our health, leaving some of us feeling afraid to gather in crowds or even touch another human being. Even our weather patterns are unreliable. We never know from one season to the next if we are actually going to experience what we have grown to expect. The Polar ice caps are diminishing. Fires, floods, and earthquakes are rampant, destroying homes and livelihoods and killing thousands. Wars continue to cycle through the Middle East and eastern Asia.

Insecurity is an epidemic in our culture leading to rampant anxiety, anger, and depression. The masses try to cope, to find some form of peace amidst the flux by over indulging in food, drugs, and alcohol or other obsessive behaviors—working too much, training too hard, getting lost in movies or a book—as a way to avoid suffering. But these only create more problems, alcoholism, obesity, anorexia , drug addictions to name a few. They mask the depressed energy running constantly on the "back burner."

Note the following statistics:

1. *Everyone* will at some time in their life be affected by depression, either their own, or someone else's. [2]

2. Depressive disorders affect about 19 - 20 million American adults. [3]

3. Pre-schoolers are the fastest growing market for anti-depressants! [4]

These numbers indicate how millions of us are living our lives backwards. Many of us believe that if circumstances were different, if we were thinner, or wealthier, or had more time, we would gain inner tranquility as well as outer comfort and happiness.

But peace and well-being rarely happen overnight.

Peace and well-being are inner states that rise from within.

Such states are associated with self empowerment. Generally we grow into them after many repetitions of thinking the same thoughts, feeling the same feelings, choosing the same choices. Step by step these repetitions become a habit.

To form this—or any kind of habit—your body and mind need this repetition. This is not esoteric. When thinking and feeling in new ways, your cells actually unplug old neuropeptides from receptor sites and plug in new ones. Voila: your biochemistry changes.

The combination of this E-Book and the accompanying audio CD will illuminate, in a practical and somatic manner, the path to peace and well being. They will lift your habitual way of being to a state of joy, lightness, and empowerment. With them, you will unlock the secrets of how to foster these feeling states on a permanent basis. Even in the midst of feeling grief, anger, depression, or disappointment, you will be able to connect to the backdrop of peace and joy behind your personal dramas.

The tools I have distilled from the *Trager* Approach will show you the way. They are not a magic pill or a quick fix. But...little by little, step by step, committing to use the tools over and over again will bring you to a state of mastery.

Mastery takes practice.

What I am asking of you is to commit to the *intention* to practice these simple tools whenever the thought pops up in your head. *That* will form a habit—a new pathway. Getting on the path is what is most important.

This path leads to empowerment. This path will show you a different way. It will change the paradigms on which you base your life. The more you develop the skills that create peace and well-being in your life, the more easily you will create "success". This is because success is an inside job.

If you put into practice the exercises in this book, and the accompanying audio downloads, the benefits you can look forward to are:

- ☑ The reduction and then "unsticking" of mental, emotional, and physical discomfort and suffering.

- ☑ A dramatic increase in your *present moment* awareness.

- ☑ Freedom from old patterns that have kept you circling in the same old ruts.

- ☑ A deepening of your consciousness and somatic connection to the Life Force, and therefore to Source, giving you a conscious anchor for stability, adaptability, and flexibility.

- ☑ The creation of a conscious dialogue with Spirit, which will allow you to be guided by its subtle promptings.

- ☑ The ability and power to transform your life in new and exciting directions.

- ☑ An increasing sense of lightness, peace, empowerment and bliss.

Many of the tools in this book have been gleaned and tailored from what Dr. Milton Trager called *Mentastics*® (coined from the two words, "mental" and "gymnastics"). By stretching the concepts, I have widened their range into exercises that are easy to use no matter who you are and no matter what you are doing.

Although I will often use the word *Mentastics*, it is important to note that I will not be asking you to become a mental pretzel, flipping and contorting like a gymnast. Instead I will ask you to practice exercises that employ your thoughts, feelings, and physicality—the three pillars that can send you along a path of ease and connection.

Not until we experience it

Is it more than just words.

After we experience it

There is no need for words.

The value of words

Is to stimulate

The desire to experience.

—MILTON TRAGER—

CHAPTER TWO

The Fundamental Element

It is stressed in every *Trager* training (and I'm sure in all artistic formal teachings) that the many "moves" and "techniques" that the student learns in their years of education are merely the craft of their trade. Just as a writer knows grammar and a guitarist knows chords, a *Trager* practitioner knows the body—its tendons, bones, and tissue. However, knowing grammar is not enough to make a best seller and knowing notes is not enough to make a hit song. Knowing the parts of the body does not make for a great *Trager* session either. To turn craft into something more, something that transcends our limited understanding, all artists, *Trager* Practitioners included, need to be able to *consciously connect* to the life-giving, life-regulating power that is all around us. This concept is integrated into a *Trager*

Practitioner's training from day one. It is for this reason that Dr. Trager would suggest we "drop the word technique."

Dr. Trager knew that his students had to let go of their training, stay out of their own way, and get into *Hook-Up* by arriving in the *present moment*. In a state of *Presence*, feelings of effortlessness, expansiveness, and joy infuse the body/mind, turning technique into a *natural* vehicle to transfer these feelings into the client's body and therefore mind.

This is why the *Trager* Approach operates through pleasurable, effortless, easy movement, which softly and safely introduces the body/mind to what it would be like if it were free to function without restriction.

Hook-Up

Dr. Milton Trager was often quoted as saying that all he really had to offer anyone was *Hook-Up* — a way to hook up or connect to the life-giving, life-regulating force that is in us and all around us. This force is nothing less than the underlying intelligence that pervades every molecule, atom, and sub-atomic particle of the entire Universe. To consciously plug into it, connect with it, and become a conduit for its flow, is at once powerful and blissful. This often repeated statement of Dr. Trager's reflected not only his ability to transfer a somatic experience of this flow into a client's body/mind, but also his humility, his knowing that the best thing that any of us can ever give anyone (including ourselves) is *Hook-Up*.

"The first step for going into Hook-Up is to acknowledge that there is a force greater than yourself." Milton Trager [5]

This force we can consciously hook up to has been described by Deepak Chopra in *The Happiness Prescription* seminar (from PBS television), as an "a-causal, non-local, quantum mechanical, interrelated field of awareness that operates with simultaneity." Breaking this down into its components: it is 'a-causal' because it has no cause; it is 'non-local' because it is beyond space time; it is 'quantum mechanical' because it is at the foundation of all things; it is 'interrelated' because every part knows what every other part is doing; and it operates with 'simultaneity' because this knowingness is instantaneous, not requiring the passage of time, exchange of energy, or information signals.

Other people might call this force God, or Source. I have two additional terms I also like to use. The first is *Unified Field*, referring to the zero-point or the reservoir of creative, intelligent potential of stillness. The second term is *Life Force*, referring to the active component manifesting throughout the universe. Whatever words work for you, they all mean the same thing.

Life force flows in the rocks and in the trees, in the birds and the animals. It is in the air that we breathe as well as the vacuum of outer space. It is in our genes, our DNA, our cells, our muscles, our bones and it is our highest purpose in this life to consciously connect with it, to become a clear conduit for this field of awareness, this life-giving life-regulating Force.

If you allow yourself, you can feel the Life Force everywhere.

As a *Trager* practitioner it is my privilege, like Dr. Trager before me, not only to *Hook-Up* personally, but to share the feeling of this connection with others: my clients, loved ones, friends, and, most importantly, those who challenge me, those I disagree with, and even those who have hurt me. Such is our greatest gift. Being conscious of, and sharing, this connection with those in our life is what I mean by *Trager as a way of living*.

An Approach

The principles of the *Trager* Approach will work for everyone, not just *Trager* practitioners or body workers. It is called an 'approach' for a reason. The principles can help you explore questions like: How can I be a better doctor? Clerk? Mother? Lover? How can I deepen my friendships? How can I more wholly open my heart to love? How can I cultivate empowerment and peace? How can I be more at ease with my body and emotions? How can I feel secure in an unstable world?

You do not even need a *Trager* Movement Re-education session to find the answers (although having one would greatly enhance your learning). Dr. Trager developed *Mentastics*, mindful movement explorations, to reap the benefits of *Trager* on your own.

Again, *Mentastics* are not about becoming a mental pretzel. Instead, they are simple, convenient tools that elicit the experience of *Hook-Up* in the body/mind at any time, and in any place or situation. As such, they can transform your approach to life.

Trager may or may not be a lightning bolt experience for you. The results are not likely to burst down from heaven into your consciousness with explosive revolutionary pizzazz, tearing open your life, leaving fragments of personality to be cleaned up and reassembled. On the contrary, the results are usually gentle, like a series of candles lit one at a time, warming and illuminating your path. Each illumination is an experience of *Hook-Up*, which turns your body/mind away from its traditional entrenchment in the past and the future, toward a new place—the *present moment*.

One moment at a time, one day at a time, one month at a time, one year at a time, you can step toward this new place, led forward by ever-deepening feelings of *Hook-Up* until you find yourself in a place of personal power, a place of sensuality and pleasure, and, most importantly, a place of increasing peace.

CHAPTER THREE

Entry Portal to *Now*

You cannot get away from it. You are always in the *present moment*. We all are. It is all there is.

The question is: Where do you put your attention?

There are only three options: the past, the future, or the present.

The past and the future are always imaginary constructs. They are in your mind. Yes, they have repercussions in the body, but that doesn't change the inexorable fact that the *Now* is all there is.

Most people perceive their life from a skewed perspective. They see themselves and the world around them through the filters of their culture, their past experiences, their beliefs, their hopes, fears, projections, and on and on. Through these filters, most of us create our lives. We might ask ourselves then, if our perception is so distorted from our past, how can we possibly bring our awareness into the *Now*?

An easy access point to *Presence* is through the body. Our body, like every other physical form, is necessarily in the *present moment* regardless of the stories we are telling ourselves or the interpretation we place on our emotions. By placing our attention on the body *without judgment* we not only arrive in the *Now*, we also become consciously aware of the Life Force flowing through everything. And, the Life Force can only be perceived in the *present moment*. You recognize the Life Force by the bodily sensations of lightness, softness, spaciousness, and ease.

There is nothing wrong with remembering the past and learning from it. There is nothing wrong with planning for the future, imagining your goals. Our challenge is that most of us put the vast majority of our attention in any place but the *present moment*. We get stuck in the past or future. This creates fear, envy, insecurity, and rigidity. Yet the *present moment* is the only place in which you can make a difference, in which you can act and build a life. We forget that the intelligent life force (which is so creative and astute it has created the diversity and infinity of the universe and all the intelligence therein) is flowing through us every moment. We forget that if we allow and foster this intelligent force to shift and manifest our lives, it will, without effort on our part, move us toward self empowerment. If we can learn to trust it, the Life Force will spin a web of wonder, abundance, good health, courage, ease, and peace.

It happens one step at a time.

Spirit

You are a trinity, a conscious being consisting of three major parts: a body, a mind, and a Spirit, that together form the unique manifestation that is you.

The part of your trinity that remains unaltered no matter what is going on is your Spirit. Your Spirit cannot be created nor destroyed. It is always there, the unbreakable thread to Source. It is the timeless and formless aspect of you that has no beginning and no end. It is the "I am", the observer, the unbiased witness to the repercussions of your body/mind. It is the part of your trinity closest to the Unified Field, the Divine Matrix, the Web of Life, or whatever you want to call the Source of life—from which all creativity and intelligence springs—your God connection.

The depth of your conscious connection to your Spirit corresponds to your level of attentiveness to the *present moment*. This is because Spirit can be directly perceived only in the *Now*. Fostering *Presence* while praying, meditating, walking, working, laughing, or crying, attunes your awareness with your Spirit. The more attuned you are to your Spirit, the more attuned you will be with the universal flow, and hence the more you will consciously create your divine expression, bringing ever-increasing levels of happiness, peace, and well-being into your life.

Mind

While Spirit exists in a state of unity, the mind and body exist in a state of duality. Spirit lies outside of the polarities of light and dark, good and bad, yin and yang, etc. The body/mind exists *within* these confines, which is why we feel cold and hot, light and heavy, sad and happy.

Spirit is eternal. It is never-changing. The body/mind is ever-changing. The body/mind is born, lives, and dies. Such is the nature of things.

Let's briefly examine the ever-changing mind.

The mind thinks. That's what it does. These thoughts are almost always concerned with the past or the future. The ego-mind attempts to define and understand a past experience, or attempts to project such definitions and understandings into the future. Sometimes this is done consciously; most often this is done unconsciously. Regardless, these thoughts soon turn into stories.

The ego-mind excels at telling stories. In fact, it is so good it can tell several stories at once. One story can be recounted in the forefront of your mind, while others play in the background—even if you are not attentive to them. At times they seem like a broken record, a never-ending stream of inner dialogue, babbling the same stories, resisting all attempts to shut them down. For many, the mind is a cacophony of confusing inner voices—an inner child, a critic, a warrior, an intuitive elder—each voice vying for centre stage, each craving your attention like a baby craves that of a parent.

Although we judge these stories as good or bad (or, for that matter, as any degree of grey in between), there is ultimately nothing inherently good or bad about them. After all, they are only thoughts, nothing more. What gives them power is our *identification* with them.

When you start identifying with the stories in your mind they become disproportionately powerful. The ego-mind blossoms. The ego-mind woos you into *belief*; woos you into accepting these stories as true, woos you into acting from the perspective of these stories. Soon your ego-mind wants every iota of your attention.

Her[2] style can range from utterly flamboyant to sly and passive-aggressive. In either case, she presupposes that she is all-important, that she is the only one that matters. From the ego-mind's point of view, she makes sense of the world. She affords you an identity. She creates your life. She is indispensable. Without her you wouldn't accomplish anything. (Or so the story goes.) As a result, the ego-mind becomes louder and more insistent. She insists on total control, usurping the other two aspects of your trinity. She ignores or re-interprets the soft, uplifting messages from your Spirit. And as for the signals rising from the body, they are often dismissed as meaningless fluff—definitely not associated with what you are thinking. With her urgency and persistence she woos you into believing that you *are* your stories.

As an adult, however, you have probably noticed that your inner dialogue has become tired and repetitive. Perhaps when you were younger your mind seemed clever and fresh, but after hearing the same old stories hundreds, or thousands, or even hundreds of

---

[2] My apologies to all women for using the pronoun 'her'. I could use 'him', in which case I'd be apologizing to all men. Our English language is limited and the ego is too personal to be an "it."

thousands of times, you must begin to wonder if the ego-mind is all she says she's cracked up to be.

Despite any reservations you may have, the ego-mind has grown accustomed to all the attention. She does not want to stop. She can't even remember what it is to stop. Your inner storyteller is out of touch with just how exhausted she is, with how uninspired she has become. She needs a break, a little R&R. Your ego-mind needs to simmer down and listen to the other two parts of your trinity—your body and your Spirit.

A fulfilled life is one that is lived from all three parts of your trinity.

The question is: How can you become unidentified or unstuck from your thoughts? Practically speaking, how can you *experience* thought as something other than you? As the saying goes, "You don't have to believe everything you think."

Body

If you want to unstick yourself from thoughts, it is counterproductive to fight or push against them. Yelling "STOP!" inside your head only reinforces the drama. What you resist persists. The way to simmer down your inner storyteller is to turn your attention away from your thoughts and toward something else: the body.

The body doesn't have thoughts. It doesn't make up stories. It simply *is*. It cannot help but be in the *Now*. As such it is automatically connected to the Life Force. Therefore, if you turn your attention away from your thoughts and toward your body you will connect as well. To be more specific, I will suggest you start by placing your attention on your body in a particular way because, in my twenty-five-year *Trager* practice, I have found that this *way* is akin to an entry portal onto the pathway to *Presence*.

You receive information through the body from both outside and inside the confines of your skin. The outside world is experienced through your senses—sight, sound, smell, taste, and touch. At any one moment there is a plethora of data coming to you through your senses. Most of this data has already been defined and categorized by your ego-mind. For example, when people see an oak tree they generally don't actually *see* the oak tree; instead they overlay on top of the experience an internal representation of "oak tree." Likewise, when you see your mother you undoubtedly don't get the reality of your "mother." Instead you perceive her through the filters of your past stories and future projections. You see her as you *think* she is.

Such filters are useful. They are short cuts that enable us to quickly make sense of our world. Without such shortcuts or filters of perception we would be lost in an avalanche of data.

The difficulty arises when we automatically assume that what we perceive through our filters is *true.* In other words, we become attached to our stories, to our interpretations of the information coming to us through our senses.

Because the mind habitually defines and categorizes what we perceive *out there*, I tell my students to start their practice by placing their attention inside the body. In general the mind has not already spun elaborate stories around the act of breathing, for example, or on the sensation of feeling weight. They are not as "sticky," which is why being attentive to your breath and the sensation of weight in your body is the entry portal to the *Now*.

CHAPTER FOUR

The Mentastics Mantra

The *Mentastics Mantra* consists of three simple tools I use every day to reduce the stickiness of my mind and turn my attention to the *Now* via the inner sensations of my body.

The *Mentastics Mantra* is the rock upon which I build my *Trager* practice and my life. I use it while giving a table session, while I lift an arm, or jiggle a thigh, or rock a belly. I use it in between the sentences I write. I use it when I go for a night out. I use it when I make love. I use it while I am gardening, while I am driving, talking to a friend, singing, or washing the dishes. I use it because, by its very nature, this *Mantra* keeps bringing me back into a moment-to-moment, body-centered awareness of what is going on right here, right now: What Dr. Trager called *Hook-Up*.

It is my hope that this simple practice will become your *Mantra* like it is mine. This *Mantra* has the potential to create spaciousness in your life, even if your days seem crammed full.

There are so many little moments to which we pay little attention, so many tiny gifts, so many fleeting blessings, so many avenues into the bliss of the *present moment*: the fresh smell of morning air after a rain, the wind gently caressing your face, the feel of your child's arms wrapped around you, the cheery chirp of a robin announcing the dawn, the colours of a sunset...

These countless blessings are a portal to feeling the aliveness of our bodies, to the immediate feeling of connection and bliss that we can easily attain when we are aware of the Life Force flowing in our muscles, joints, and tissues.

Consider that you are a consciousness inhabiting a living thing. Your body has its own consciousness. Without you having to be aware of it, the body repairs itself, digests food, sweats toxins, replicates cells, fights disease, sheds skin—a myriad of processes that in and of themselves have levels of consciousness. We are a consciousness living within systems of consciousnesses. Life within life. When you are able to feel this, to live this, it is wondrous.

At first blush, the *Mentastics Mantra* will not seem particularly profound. But it is. By understanding and using this practice, the way you perceive your life will transform. The moments of your life will change from dissonance to resonance, from chaos to harmony.

But before I go into the nuances of this *Mantra*, let me first ask that you give yourself permission to be a beginner. Allow yourself not to know the answers right away. Be at peace, without being an immediate pro. Foster acceptance when you find yourself "stuck."

Take the attitude of a beginner. This will facilitate the process of learning, allowing knowledge to unfold in its own time without taking the wrong turns associated with premature judgments of how we think something *should* be. Don't be concerned with how things *should* be. That is irrelevant. Enjoy the process of your own unfolding by taking off the pressure. From this lighter perspective, your initial foray into the unknown will be easier.

There are three parts to the *Mentastics Mantra*. Although I will approach each part separately, in reality they work in concert. They combine and flow into each other in an organic process. Together they will form the foundational habit of being in the *Now*, living life from every aspect of our trinity.

Two parts of the *Mentastics Mantra* I have already briefly touched upon: attention to breath, and attention to the sensation of weight in your body. The other part is...

Pausing

A pause interrupts momentum.

A pause disrupts your moving and spinning.

A pause opens your awareness.

A pause refreshes you.

A pause allows for possibility.

A pause: such a little thing, a simple thing. So small, yet so difficult to do!

My experience as a teacher is that this simple little thing—pausing—is the biggest challenge. You might know in your mind how beneficial a pause might be. You might consciously tell yourself you want it. When you actually remember to pause, however, suddenly a myriad of reasons arise as to why you should pause *after* you've finished that email, *after* you've washed the floor, *after* you've brushed your teeth. The moment you want to create a slice of stillness, the inner chatter gets louder. This is because your request is often tainted (consciously or unconsciously) with the frustrated desire to stuff a sock in the storyteller's mouth. This desire is partly why beginners often find meditation a bit of a let-down; they want the chattering inner voice to be silenced all at once.

Instead, be easy. Start out with baby steps.

Quit the chattering for just a moment. A moment only.

You have the power.

A slice of stillness is within your reach this moment. Take a single second right now. Yes, now. Stop reading, look ahead or close your eyes, and ... *pause*.

Did the pause last a second? A micro-second? Several seconds? Longer? Whatever length, celebrate. Through that pause is the path to your empowerment, to your freedom, to your peace.

Now:

1. *Close your eyes.*

2. *Bring your attention to your breath. Feel your chest expanding and contracting. The air flowing in and out. It doesn't matter if it's shallow or deep, fast or slow. Simply notice...*

3. *...notice the space between the in-breath, and out-breath.*

4. *The space between the out-breath, and in-breath.*

5. *Stillness lies here.*

6. *Now, open your eyes.*

(You can also follow along with *Pausing* track 1 on the audio download *Pathway to Presence*.)

Congratulations. You've just become consciously aware of one of the many pauses that are always happening within you. I propose you use your power to create little pauses throughout your day. Don't dwell on them. Don't plan them, or schedule them, or create a philosophy about them. All these things are storytelling tactics designed to distract you. Simply, without drama, pause...whenever you remember.

Yes, it's that easy. Everything else is melodrama and story.

Little Moments

Consider waiting in a slow-moving line at the grocery store. Instead of fretting over your inability to move forward—your ego-voice belting out old repetitive reactions of frustration, anxiety, and worry —take a moment and... *Pause.*

Consider walking toward your supervisor's office where you are to deliver a report you've been working on for weeks. Maybe you are stressed and worried about whether she will approve, about whether you've done it 'right.' Just before you get to her door, slow your momentum and... *Pause.*

Consider that you are feeling on top of the world. You've become top sales person for the month, bringing you extra money for that vacation you've been yearning to take. You and your life partner have just celebrated a dozen loving years together. You feel loved, confident and empowered, and know that you can accomplish anything you put your mind to. Take a moment and... *Pause.*

Consider that someone has done something to upset you. Maybe they've cut you off in traffic. Maybe a friend has made a callous comment veiled as a joke. Maybe your mother-in-law has pushed one of your buttons. As you feel your frustration and anger rising, take a moment and... *Pause.*

Every time you remember, in all areas of your life, create slices of stillness. Don't worry if your inner chattering voice constantly craves your attention. Don't worry about the content of the dialogue. Don't try to control her. Instead, just for a moment...*Pause.*

Keep it simple.

Mindful Umbrella Breathing

The purpose of the next two parts in the *Mentastics Mantra* is to bring your awareness through a pause and into your inner body, the entry portal to the *Now*.

The second step of the *Mantra* is quite natural, so natural in fact, you are already doing it. While in the midst of a pause, bring your attention to your breath.

Spirit, your unique energy signature, can be experienced as riding the rhythm of your breath. Many traditional meditations suggest attentiveness to breath. It invites a clearer connection. Mindful attention to your breath deepens the physical sensation of the life-giving, life-regulating force that is all around you. It tends to draw you into your centre, the hub of your wheel of life, away from the outer rim where activities keep you in a whirl.

Bringing your attention to your breath is useful because breath doesn't usually have meaning attached to it. To the mind it is neutral and therefore supports a pause, a quieting of the stories banging around in your head. When you place your attention on your breath while in the midst of a pause, your slice of stillness will lengthen and deepen.

To increase the power of this exercise, I'm going to ask that you be attentive to your breath in a particular way. I'm going to ask that you employ your imagination.

Imagine an umbrella with the rod pointing upward, opening and closing three dimensionally.

Open, close. Expand, contract.

Now take this three dimensional imagining and combine it with your physical breath. As you breathe in, imagine the umbrella opening in a three hundred and sixty degree circle. No need to put your attention on the central rod of the umbrella, only the round material covering. As you exhale, close the umbrella.

Inhale. Exhale.

Open your umbrella. Breathe into your chest, your back, and your sides. Feel energy rush into every nook and cranny of your lungs and rib cage. Close your umbrella. Breathe out, allowing full room for fresh air to re-enter.

This exercise helps you become aware of aspects of your body to which you might not have been paying attention before. In the past you may have really felt only the front of your chest, having much less awareness of the back. Or if you were aware of your back, maybe you only had partial awareness of your side ribs. Mindful Umbrella Breathing is like switching from mono to surround sound. It will give your breath extra depth. It will noticeably expand your slice of stillness and get you more in touch with the physical sensation of the life-giving, life-regulating force that is all around us.

The following is the second exercise of the three-part *Mentastics Mantra*.

(If you can, follow along with *Mindful Umbrella Breathing* track 2 on the audio download *Pathway to Presence*.)

Mindful Umbrella Breathing

1. *To begin, sit or stand comfortably.*

2. *Take a moment to recall the stillness you experienced while pausing.*

3. *Now, bring your attention to your breath. Feel your chest expanding and contracting. The air flowing in and out. It doesn't matter if it's shallow or deep, fast or slow. Simply notice...*

4. *As you breathe in, invite the Life Force to rise from the earth through imaginary golden roots attached to the bottoms of your feet. And as you breathe out, allow any fatigue and tension to drain away.*

5. *Continue to imagine your in-breath, travelling up through your feet and legs, flowing into your pelvic girdle, and permeating your belly. With your out-breath, let go of all your worries and judgements.*

6. *Now, with your in-breath, bring this life-giving energy into your diaphragm, all the way up into your chest, your shoulders relaxed and down.*

7. *As you exhale, release any inadequacies, burdens and strife.*

8. *As your breath continues, allow a pause to enter...*

9. *Softly notice how you feel.*

10. *Now, imagine that your chest is an umbrella, with the tip pointing upward toward the top of your head. Breathe in, opening the umbrella in a 360-degree circle—expand your front, your back, and your sides. Breathe out, closing the umbrella—expel your tired deoxygenated air.*

11. *Continue to breathe in and out of your umbrella. As it expands, become aware of the energy travelling up your torso, along your arms, and out your hands. As your umbrella contracts, allow any trauma, fatigue, or pain to leave your body in a sound...ahhhh.*

12. *Now pause...notice how you are feeling.*

13. *Innocently bring your attention back to your umbrella breathing.*

14. *With your in-breaths, imagine energy flowing up through your entire body: from your roots, into your legs and hips, up your torso, hands and arms, into your neck, spilling out the top of your head, like a fountain of water. Take your time. Make it as real as you can.*

15. *Now, with your out-breaths, imagine pulling energy down from the heavens through your entire body: into your crown, head, and neck, down your torso, arms and hands, your hips, your legs; flushing out any remnants of suffering and draining it through your feet, into the earth to be cleansed. Again, take your time.*

16. *Your whole body is an umbrella now. Every part of you expands and contracts with each breath. Gently notice the life-giving, life-regulating energy travelling up and down, in and out....*

17. *Pause... Notice how you feel.*

18. *Stay with this circuit to connect even more deeply with Spirit, the central thread of your being, the hub of your wheel.*

Little Moments

Consider getting shocking news. There has been an accident and a person close to you is in critical condition in the hospital. Pause… and breathe into your "umbrella." Just for now, let everything go except your pause and your breath. Continue until your balance point changes.

Consider being nervous before a presentation. You feel your whole career is riding on your performance. Your palms are sweaty and your heart feels like it will thump right out of your chest. Pause… and breathe into your "umbrella." Just for now, let the chatter go. There is only your pause, your breath, and a sense of aliveness. Do it again…and again, if you need to, until clarity and calmness return.

Consider feeling overwhelmed because you have too many tasks and not enough time to do them: Johnny needs to be picked up from school, you have a dentist appointment, little Suzy has piano lessons, all within the hour. Pause… and breathe into your umbrella. Let go of your whirling mind. Feel the flow of the Life Force moving through you as you pause and mindfully breathe into your umbrella. Continue for a few moments until harmony returns.

While Pausing is the all important first ingredient, mindful umbrella breathing is the second ingredient in the *Mentastics Mantra*. It will widen your slice of stillness and grow a conscious connection with your inner sensations.

Now, to add the third ingredient...

Feeling Weight

Generally speaking, feeling the weight of a part of your body does not have a lot of stories attached to it. Like breathing, it's neutral. When you bring attention to the weight of your arm, let's say, it doesn't usually trigger an escalation of inner chatter.

Our nervous system, which branches out from our spinal column and into the far extremities of our body, is the structure, along with our brain, that gives us somatic sensations, like feeling weight. The feeling of weight is perceived all through the body—through tissue, bones, joints, tendons and ligaments—as these parts move through space. Consider for a moment just how many components work together to bring you the coordinated sensations of feeling weight. The simple act of walking—feeling your feet on the ground, your arms swinging at your sides, your hips shifting from one side to the other, the flow of your right side to your left—entails a multitude of these structures working in concert, communicating with each other in never-ending feedback loops. In this light, such a seemingly simple act as picking up a can of beans is a stunning act of magnificent complexity!

Consider that you have an important decision concerning your aging mother. She wants her independence but needs to live in a residence that provides constant care. Your family is counting on you to make the right decision. You've studied all the options from every angle, over and over again, until you're ready to explode. What to do? What to do?

Take yourself for a walk. Not to ponder a decision, but just to go for a walk—that simple. A longer walk outdoors is ideal, but even a short walk up and down your hallway will work.

- *As you are walking, feel the weight roll from your heels through your toes.*

- *Notice the sway of your hips as the weight slides from one side to the other.*

- *Feel the weight of your tail bone as if you have an imaginary tail that trails on the ground, swishing behind you.*

- *Feel the weight of your arms swinging by your sides.*

- *All of a sudden you feel softer, your steps are lighter, your head clearer. You feel energized from the walk rather than drained.*

Feeling the weight of some part of your body connects you with gravity, and gravity can only be experienced in the *here* and *now*. Your ligaments, joints, and tendons don't make up stories about what it feels like to raise your arm. Your tissue doesn't hypothesize about what it means to feel the weight of your foot. By its very nature, your body is *always* in the *present moment*.

This is a powerful point.

The *"present moment"* nature of the body, combined with the inherent storytelling neutrality of feeling weight, makes the third aspect of the *Mentastics Mantra* elegantly simple yet power-packed.

When you bring an open attentiveness to the weight of your body, to its multiple interconnected and seamless parts moving through space—riding a bicycle, walking down the sidewalk, sitting in a chair, putting away the groceries—you get an ever-deepening awareness of the Life Force in your physicality.

Try the next *Mentastics* on for size.

(Also follow along with *Feeling Weight* track 3 on the audio download *Pathway to Presence*.)

1. *Stand with your feet shoulder width apart.*

2. *Pause... Picture a window in your mind. Open it. Allow any thoughts to be carried away on a warm seaside breeze.*

3. *Breathe into your umbrella, opening it in a 360 degree circle—expand your front, your back, and your sides. Breathe out, closing your umbrella. In and out, keeping your shoulders relaxed and down... in and out...in and out...*

4. *Now, slowly and gently, without twisting, shift your weight from side to side... slowly... one foot to the other... Notice the weight as it shifts through the little bones in your feet. You are not here to judge... just notice.....*

5. *Notice how the weight shifts through your ankles... notice the weight shift through your calves... your knees... your hips... Feel the weight in the floor of your pelvis as it slides from side to side. Just notice...*

6. *Now, bring your attention to your ribcage as you breathe into your umbrella... in and out... Notice your weight as it shifts from one side of your ribs to the other... Shift your attention upward to your shoulders. Feel the weight of your arms and hands hanging... If you can, feel the weight of your fingers too...*

7. *Open your mouth and feel the weight of your jaw as you continue shifting your body from side to side...*

8. *Feel the weight of your ears—first one and then the other...*

9. *Feel the weight of each half of your brain, one side and then the other...*

10. *As you continue shifting, expand your attention to encompass your whole body. Experience your entire body shifting as a unit. Take your time... move deeply into the experience...*

11. *Now slowly come to centre and bring your movement to a close. Allow yourself to pause... breathe into your umbrella... notice how you feel.*

12. *Next, gently shift your weight backward and forward—just until you feel the weight of your heels and just until you feel the weight of your toes. Stay comfortably within your balance; don't knock yourself off centre. Notice how your weight shifts differently going in this direction.*

13. *As you continue shifting within your range of balance, notice the weight in the front of your jaw and the back of your neck... Notice the weight in your collar bones and shoulder blades... your belly and lower back... the front of your knees and the back of your knees... heels and toes...*

14. *As you continue shifting back and forth, expand your awareness to encompass your whole body. Experience your entire body shifting as a unit. Take your time...*

15. *Again, slowly come to centre and bring your movement to a close. Allow yourself to pause... breathe into your umbrella... Notice how you feel?*

Feeling weight ties into so many other things: the conscious, interconnected relationship of body and mind, your emotions, the emotional state of a situation, and the holding patterns you unconsciously carry in your body, to name a few. All of these tie-ins are robust enough subjects that some have entire sections of this book devoted to them.

In Concert

You have now been introduced to the three aspects of the *Mentastics Mantra*: 1. Pausing, 2. Umbrella Breathing, and 3. Feeling Weight. Each is powerful in its own right. But when you use them in concert, they become one of the easiest and most profound tools you can have to access the *Now*.

Don't be fooled by their simplicity. That is the key to their success. "Do less and accomplish more," has become one of my favorite sayings. Nature always finds the path of least resistance. Drop the idea that complex and difficult is more worthwhile than simple and easy.

A pause is simple. So whenever you remember just...pause. Notice your chest opening and closing, like an umbrella. Then put your awareness on the weight of some part of your body as it hangs or moves through space. By doing these three things in concert you enter the portal to the *Now*.

By its very nature, this three-part *Mantra* helps you to become unidentified or unstuck from your thoughts. It gives you a physical *experience* (not an intellectual concept) of what Dr. Trager calls *Hook-Up*, that connection to the life-giving, life-regulating force that is all around us.

Keep bringing your attention back to the *Mentastics Mantra* as you go through your day. Don't worry which tool to use first. If you happen to notice the weight of your grocery bag first, which reminds you to breathe into your umbrella, which induces a long yummy pause—that's great. The order of the *Mantra* is irrelevant. The three tools are meant to be used as a unit, one reinforcing the other, creating ever increasing moments of stillness and connection.

Traditionally, the way to foster moments of inner stillness is through prayer or meditation. With prayer or meditation, you take a pre-set time with the specific intention to bring stillness into your conscious mind. They are disciplines specifically tailored to lower the volume on your inner chatter so you can talk to, or listen to, the Spirit aspect of your trinity.

Over the centuries many wise people have spoken eloquently about the benefits of these practices which naturally deepen your awareness of what is going on inside. They are valuable practices. In fact, I teach a body-centered meditation in my workshops, *The Power of Presence* and *Six Simple Steps to the Now*.

But while it is important to practice stillness as you sit in a quiet room, it is just as important—if not more so—to insert moments of stillness throughout your day, while working, walking, washing the dishes, dancing, talking, playing—anything. The *Mentastics Mantra* is designed to do this. It is designed to foster a somatic, conscious experience of the Life Force, anywhere, anyplace, anytime. This is profound. Transformative. Paradigm shifting.

But it takes practice. Mastery of anything takes practice.

Again, I ask you to commit to the *intention* to practice these three simple tools whenever the thought pops up in your head. *That* will form a habit—a new pathway.

Remember, getting on the path is what is most important.

Little Moments

Consider being in rush hour traffic after a long day at work. It's hot. You're tired. Perspiration trickles down your back. A headache threatens. All you want to do is get home and out of those sticky work-clothes and into something cool and comfortable. Maybe even make yourself a nice refreshing drink. But reality bites. You are stuck in a long line of idling, fume-belching cars. To your great dismay you find out that the blockage is caused by an accident up ahead! It will be hours until it's cleared up. Your shoulders start creeping up. Soon they are nearly to your ears. Your nostrils flair as your breath comes in short gasps. Your headache blossoms, feeling like it is splitting your head in two. What to do??

Feel the weight of your shoulders and elbows hanging off the steering wheel. Notice how open your chest becomes as you breathe into your umbrella. Pause. Do it again. Breathe. Pause. Notice. You feel your shoulders drop. The base of your neck softens. A thought bubble gently pops into your head, *This is an opportunity*. Your next breath is luxurious. Your body changes its emotional vibe. You become aware of your connection. *Ahh…*

Consider your child is due at the auditorium in a mere fifteen minutes. Your spouse is late. How could he be late! Tonight is the performance! Your jaw is clenched tight and so is your forehead. You pace back and forth in front of the window and then…you remember. You feel the weight of your jaw and the back of your neck. *Ahh…*a deep cleansing breath escapes. You pause. Despite the time crunch you take a second. You feel the weight of your house keys in your hand. A moment later the car pulls into the driveway. *Fourteen minutes*, you think. *No problem.*

Using the *Mentastics Mantra* opens the portal, in a somatic way, to the *Now*, to the gateway of a path that will lead you to Spirit. These three tools—pausing, umbrella breathing, and feeling weight—used together are your foundational practice. Come back to them again and again as you go through your days. You don't have to practice them for long periods of time. On the contrary, it's best if you have a lot of little moments interspersed throughout your day. Practice the *Mantra* along side everything you do, including reading the next section of this book, because in it we will explore a much stickier subject: emotions.

CHAPTER FIVE

Something Stickier

As I said in the beginning of this book, our greatest challenge is that most of us spend the vast majority of our time in any place but the *present moment*. We get stuck in the past or future. We get *attached.*

Attachment is what takes you out of *Presence.* Attachment to past forms of the never-ending, ever-unfolding stream of experience is the root of our suffering. The aim of this book is to loosen your attachments.

One of the things we hold deep attachment to is our emotions.

Emotions overlay every aspect of our lives: our personality, our job, our relationships, our appearance, and so on. If we can learn to lessen our attachment to our emotions, then, by extension, our attachment to everything else lessens too.

Emotions are ripe with stories. In fact, many of us don't know how to experience emotion without putting a story to it—it's *that* automatic. The stronger the emotion, the bigger impact the story has on our life. These emotions/stories rule us. They often overwhelm us. Without even investigating their validity, we *identify* with them.

Emotions have a whole other level of stickiness. If breath and weight have a stickiness factor of 2 out of 10, then emotions are an 11!

For this reason I once again ask that you give yourself permission to be a beginner. In the territory of emotions it is even more important to allow yourself to *not know*. You do not need to be an immediate expert. Allow yourself to let go of what you "think" you know. Observe your inner life with a fresh perspective.

E-Motion

Emotion is nothing more than energy in motion (E-*motion*) flowing through your body. Yes, that's all.

You can feel this if you put your attention there.

Try it right now. It will only take a second.

Allow for a pause. Feel your umbrella breath, and the weight of your tail bone.

Allow your pause to go deeper...

Bring your attention to the energy running through your body. There is no need to judge it. Simply say, "Hi there." You'll notice that you are, in fact, feeling *something*. This something will be perceived as a flow happening in some part (or all) of your body.

Take a moment...

Now, if you haven't already, go ahead and define the predominant emotion you are feeling. Put a word, or series of words, to this flow of energy.

Take another moment...

What came up for you? Are you feeling happy, sad, frustrated, exuberant, depressed? Some combination of these? Or are you humming along in neutral?

Now, whatever the definition, ask yourself *why* you are experiencing this flow of emotion?

Take yet another moment...

If you're like most people, you'll have had no problem coming up with the *why*. There always seems to be a reason for an emotional response. My manager didn't acknowledge my hard work. My kids are so frustrating. My husband brought me a dozen roses—for no reason! I got cut off in traffic. I sprained my knee last week. I'm always affected by the barometric pressure. I was born this way.

Automatically our body/mind generates a particular emotional response in reaction to a particular situation. This reaction reinforces the "why." It is this self perpetuating circuit that we believe justifies our attachment.

But really, our emotions are nothing more than energy in motion in our bodies. As such they have no predefined meaning.

This energy constantly flows through our bodies whether our minds are aware of it or not. Like the weather, emotions are always here. Sometimes they're sunny, sometimes they're cloudy, but *something* is always happening.

Also like the weather, emotions take on recurring patterns, patterns that have a specific vibration. As young children we learned to understand these patterns by applying labels to them. At first emotions were fuzzy, vague, and confusing, but in time you learned what it was to "be angry," or "be happy," or "be bored."

But what if these labels, upon which much of your emotional perceptions are based, were somehow skewed, and are now inaccurate and disempowering?

Different Labels, Different Results

Imagine a pair of identical twins, named Daniel and David. They are impish, freckled five-year olds with cowlicks springing from mops of coppery red hair. They are about to step on stage for the first time to perform a play called *Green Cheese Pie*. David will be the captain of a space ship that flies to the moon. Daniel will be the scientist whose job it is to collect samples of the green cheese. It's their first time on stage.

The day of the performance the twins feel funny. It's as if insects are buzzing around in their bellies. Their hearts seem like they will pound right out of their chests. Their hands feel cold and clammy and they feel like they have a lump in their throat. Their faces are hot. They've never experienced these feelings before so can't put words to these sensations. Without a context through which to apply meaning, they simply feel "funny."

Before Daniel heads back stage his father comes up to him. "How are you feeling?" he asks.

Daniel shrugs his shoulders. "Dunno."

"Well, you must be scared. I would be," says the father, rolling his eyes. "Don't worry about feeling nervous or anxious, though. Just go up there and do the best you can."

Then the mother comes up to David and asks the same question.

Like his brother, David shrugs his shoulders. "Dunno."

"Well, if I were you," says the mother, smiling, "I'd be excited and psyched. My body would be buzzing, my hands would be clammy, and I'd *know* I was ready to do my very best!"

Here, both brothers have a very similar experience. But Daniel and David now have different initial frames of reference for the experience. Daniel will now interpret similar future emotions as "anxious" or "nervous" or "scared." David on the other hand will interpret the same energy as "excited" and "psyched." To David, this pattern tells him he *will* do his best.

From this initial seemingly benign experience, Daniel is heading down a road called "stage fright," a road that entails all kinds of personal discomfort when stepping up in public. David, on the other hand, is on the road to loving being in the spotlight. It will pump him up and allow his creativity to flow. Comparatively speaking, he'll be better equipped to wow an audience.

This simple story shows how more than one label can be applied to an emotional pattern. It also shows that our labels are, for better or worse, often given to us by well-meaning parents, friends, and teachers.

Mislabeling Emotional Patterns

Becky is a delicate, angelic looking six-year-old. Usually she is quite talkative, her thin hands animating her speech. But today she is silent. She slumps over her bowl of soggy breakfast cereal, her golden hair skimming the surface of the milk. She sniffs. Her index finger rubs her raw red nose. She doesn't notice, but her sweater is on in-side-out.

In her mind Becky has been re-playing a scene that happened over two weeks ago. She was readying the family's new puppy, Grover, for a walk. She had to put on Grover's collar. Her mother had told her to make it tight, but Becky was concerned for Grover's comfort and so left a little breathing room. (Grover was such a good dog; he deserved it.) After clipping on the leash, she headed out the door. She skipped along pretending to play hopscotch, all the while explaining to her puppy the rules of the game. Suddenly a large cat sprang from out behind a cedar hedge with a surprised yowl.

Grover barked and lunged, trying to get at the cat. Becky yelled "Stay!" But Grover didn't listen and continued to twist and yank until he slipped his collar.

Becky immediately ran after the puppy. Though small, Grover was fast and quickly outdistanced her. She saw him sprint into a neighbor's back yard. "Grover!" she yelled in her biggest outdoor voice.

By the time she burst breathless into the backyard, the dog was gone. Her eyes darted around. She checked behind the shed. "Grover! Grover!" Behind the bush. "Grover!" Behind the garden.

The owners of the house opened their back door. "What's all this yelling? What's going on?"

Becky whipped around. There was an intense welling from her stomach into her throat, combined with an empty sinking feeling in her belly. "I've lost my dog!" she cried. "Help!"

Grover never was found. But the welling in Becky's throat and the empty sinking sensation in her belly did not go away. The picture of that empty back yard haunts her. She has no interest in her breakfast cereal. No interest at all.

Becky's mom hurries into the kitchen, rummaging through her purse. She looks up, sees a pathetic Becky, and the purse falls, its contents scattering across the linoleum. "Look what I've done. I'm *so* late," she mutters, then glances up at Becky and changes her tone. "Come on Honey-pie. You haven't touched your cereal."

Becky doesn't move or answer.

Her mom gives a heavy sigh as she stuffs the last items back into her bag. "Becky I know you're grieving sweetheart. I know it hurts to lose something you love. But...but sometimes you have to let it go. It's been two weeks. It's time to accept it. Loss is a part of life." Her mom grasps Becky's shoulders and pulls her erect. She kisses her daughter's forehead and says, "Now, put on a smile. You don't want to miss your bus."

Notice how Becky's mom just put the labels "grieve" and "hurt" on Becky's emotional pattern (a welling in her throat and a sinking emptiness in her belly). This isn't a bad thing. It helps the child understand what she is feeling. But sometimes, such a label is incorrect.

The truth is Becky has not started to grieve; what she is really feeling is shame and guilt. Her mother doesn't suspect this because Becky told her that she put the collar on tight.

A few months later the family gets another puppy, but every time Becky sees this dog she is reminded of Grover and feels bad. Becky stays distant and detached from this new puppy because, by this time, shame, guilt, and grieving are all wrapped up together.

As a result, Becky continues to feel shame and guilt whenever she grieves the loss of something or someone she loves. It doesn't matter that she's not to blame. It doesn't matter that her goldfish dies of old age. It doesn't matter that her first real boyfriend's hormones are raging, which is why he dumps her for another girl thirteen days, four hours, and twenty minutes after their magical first kiss.

Before Becky's sixteenth birthday these (and other) experiences morph into a belief that says, *"It's my fault people leave me."* By this time she's armored herself against these hurts. She's gained sixty pounds, stiffened the posture of her whole upper body, and started dressing in dark formidable clothing, all in an unconscious attempt to protect herself.

As an adult Becky has lost her childhood talkativeness and has trouble with intimacy. She doesn't know why.

Through these scenarios (Daniel's, David's, and Becky's) you can see how easy it is to mislabel emotions. How we *think* we are feeling might not be accurate. This inaccuracy leads to erroneous and disempowering beliefs that can give rise to unforeseen difficulties. The inner storyteller replays the same scenes and retells the same stories to the corresponding emotional patterns. In this way the whole process becomes entrenched and *sticky*. We identify with this powerful self-perpetuating circuit to such a degree that many of us say, "It's just who I am." Without knowing it, we become *attached*.

So, how can we unstick ourselves from such labels? How can we perceive e-motion as the mutable and changing thing it is?

Labeling: A Personal Perspective

Rarely has money been a priority in my life; my spiritual life has always come first. But occasionally I find myself engulfed by poverty consciousness. One such occasion occurred only a few months ago.

Just before I headed out the door en route to the neighborhood mall to pick up a few groceries, I saw my landlord slowly shuffling down the walkway toward me in his old baggy clothes, looking like the retired Spanish immigrant carpenter he was. He gave me a brief, sheepish smile and then started to say something in his thick, heavy accent that sounded as if he had a handful of marbles in his mouth.

"Pardon?" I asked.

Then I figured it out: he was raising our rent. Again. For the fourth year in a row!

The conversation lasted thirty seconds and then he was gone, but by the end of it my insides were bubbling. Adrenaline rushed into my system. A few minutes later I slammed the front door and marched to the mall. As I stomped, my eyes narrowed. My teeth clamped. My shoulders tightened. *Greedy bastard!* I thought. It wasn't like he actually took care of the place. The fences were falling down, the roof of the garage leaked like a sieve, the windows were single-paned, the appliances barely worked, the kitchen faucet dripped non-stop, and our heating bills had just quadrupled because *he* refused to replace the broken heat pump, which meant we had to use an ancient backup oil furnace that stank and spewed pollution into the atmosphere all winter long. And, we're the ones keeping up with repairs and tending the yard and gardens without so much as a dime from him.

In the midst of my storyteller's rant, the Spirit aspect of my trinity whispered, *You have no direct control here. All you're doing is creating internal suffering.*

But it's so unfair! exclaimed my storyteller.

I know, whispered Spirit.

This feeling is real, said my storyteller. *I'm not going to ignore it.*

Walk your talk, said the whisper. *Remove the labels and simply feel the e-motion without the story, without the why.*

I stepped off the sidewalk and onto the grass of a park located between my house and the mall. I employed the *Mentastics Mantra*. I took a deep breath, feeling the expansion and contraction of my chest like an umbrella opening and closing, and ... paused. I did it again. And again. Then I felt my weight, as I shifted from side to side, side to side, attentive to my feet on the ground. The story melted away. The ugly words that had demanded supremacy, evaporated. I felt my emotions as simply energy in motion.

After a few moments I asked, *What other kind of label could I apply to this energy?* Words like "power" and "aliveness" jumped to mind. I checked in. If I removed the story, these labels were just as accurate as "anger" and "righteousness."

Still in the park, I paused again, and repeated the *Mentastics Mantra*. I let go of these new labels and once more felt the energy moving through my body, this time without meaning.

After a couple of minutes I asked the same question: *What other kind of label could I apply to this energy?* Then I waited with Beginner's Mind, with innocence and non-assumption.

Just like the last time, the words "power" and "aliveness" came forward.

These new labels didn't change the situation from unfair to fair. They didn't make the rent increase go away. But by feeling my e-motions as simply energy in motion through my body I was given a choice. I could choose to wallow in victimhood, or I could choose to apply new labels (which over time, lead to new beliefs).

To be doubly sure of my choice, I felt the weight of these labels in my mind. In one hand I had "anger" and "righteousness," in the other I had "power" and "aliveness." *Which felt lighter?* I asked. *Which felt more aligned with Spirit?*

There was no contest.

In that moment I realized (perhaps for the thousandth time) that the definitions and boundaries I unconsciously put around my emotions aren't set in stone. In fact they are quite fluid.

Changing Shape

Becky, the angelic six-year old, mislabeled her emotions. She didn't have the experience to come to a precise description and, as she got older, she simply assumed that her first childhood labels were accurate. In the encounter with my landlord, however, I didn't mislabel my emotions. I simply came at them from a particular perspective (poverty consciousness). Such perspectives can be changed if you realize that e-motion is just energy in motion, without predetermined meanings.

However, not only are the labels we place on emotions fluid, so are the emotions themselves. You can actually change your internal energy patterns. We have all experienced this at one time or another even though we might not have been consciously aware of what we were actually doing. For example, when we feel down and depressed we might automatically go to the garden to pull a few weeds, or go for a run, or vacuum the floor. We don't necessarily make a conscious choice about the fluidity of our emotional patterns but we know that doing something else often changes things.

Try this *Mentastics* Exercise and feel what I mean.

(Also follow along with *Feeling Energy Patterns* track 4 on the audio download *Pathway to Presence*.)

1. *Give yourself permission to be a beginner. Let go of your inner perfectionist.*

2. *Now, Pause...innocently listen to the stillness within.*

3. *Breathe into your umbrella. Open it up...close it down, open and close. Allow your breathing to happen effortlessly.*

4. *Whether you are sitting or standing, feel your weight as you shift from side to side becoming aware of the aliveness of the Life Force flowing through your body.*

5. *Now, become stationary.*

6. *Get comfortable.*

7. *Close your eyes.*

8. *Take a few moments to recall a recent experience that evoked a strong emotion.*

9. *Imagine being there again. If you can, be in the middle of the experience. Take your time.*

10. *What do you see? Hear? Smell? Feel?*

11. *How would you define the emotion you are feeling right now? Put a label on it. Angry? Depressed? Playful?*

12. *Bring awareness to this feeling. Where in your body is this feeling located? Your chest? Your head? Your belly? Someplace else?*

13. *What shape does it have?*

14. *What does it weigh?*

15. *Is it vibrating?*

16. *Does it have texture?*

17. *Smell?*

18. *Colour?*

19. *Do not judge this experience. Just be innocently aware of whatever is happening for you.*

20. *Now, start to play with this energy within your body.*

21. *Imagine it a different shape.*

22. *Imagine it a different colour. Alter the texture. Change the weight. If it's vibrating, change its rate. Take a few moments to feel all of these changes in your body. How would you interpret this emotion now?*

23. *Okay, dissolve the boundaries of this pattern. Let its energy spread like warm oil through your entire body.*

24. *Check in. Has your interpretation of this energy changed again?*

25. *Now, imagine this energy draining into the earth like water soaking into the ground.*

26. *Gently open your eyes. Bring awareness to the bottoms of your feet.*

27. *Notice your breath expanding and contracting.*

28. *Embrace the changeable and flexible nature of your emotional experiences.*

Just about everyone who does this exercise can play with their emotions to one degree or another. Some make only small modifications while others shift their internal energy patterns with gusto. Whether you are immediately accomplished or not, it doesn't matter. What matters is that you *could* make a change. What matters is that you now know that your emotions are not static. Just like your labels, your emotions are fluid and mutable. Let go of your static relationship with emotions. Allow for the possibility that your emotions can become the bliss and power fueling your life.

CHAPTER SIX

Paradigm Shifting Answers

By practicing the *Mentastics Mantra* in as many areas of your life as you can, you will deepen your awareness of the *present moment*. Your feelings of insecurity and helplessness in these dramatic changing times will lessen and dwindle. The more you live your life in *Presence*, the more stability, flexibility, adaptability and clarity will enter your life, awakening peace and empowerment within you.

Awakening is a natural part of your process as a human being.

The lessons in this chapter will accelerate this growth even more. You will be given an easy step-by-step process to consciously co-create your evolution with Spirit. You will learn to elicit change for your highest good, without perpetuating the past. Like the *Mentastics*

Mantra, this process is deceptively simple. All you do is ask a question of Spirit.

However, to ask a question of Spirit and get paradigm-shifting results requires that you ask (and receive) from Spirit in a very specific way. When we ask in this way we use our unconscious mind as a conduit to Spirit. The trick is not to make demands, or, for that matter , pleas. "Please take this pain away." "Make my husband more affectionate." "Help me earn more money." Demands or pleas don't work. Instead its about accessing the intelligence all around you so that this intelligence (not your ego) leads you on your journey of personal evolution.

There are five steps involved in asking questions in this way.

The **first step** is to know *to whom* you are directing your questions. If you want to explore new answers to old dilemmas, if you want to discover alternative labels to entrenched emotional patterns, if you want to grow toward empowerment and peace, there is only one place to direct your questions: to Spirit.

Spirit is the all-knowing, never-changing part of our trinity. Spirit is in tune with the intelligence that is all around us. Spirit is not entrapped by our past experiences and misconceptions. Spirit is the only part of our trinity that can lead us forward in fresh and unanticipated directions. The way out of our ego-box is through Spirit.

The most effective way to ask a question of Spirit is to go *where* Spirit resides, where you can clearly receive the answer: the *present moment*. This is the **second step**.

Use the *Mentastics Mantra* and release your past and future. Pause, breath mindfully, and feel the weight of some part of your body to unstick yourself from your inner stories and associated labels. Repeat the *Mantra* as many times as necessary to step into the *present moment*. Become the observer. Detach yourself from the melodrama of your storyteller's voice. Notice the energy patterns running through your body. Just notice.

Once in *Presence*, the **third step** is to actually *ask* your question. But the question needs to be open-ended. Allow room in your question for Spirit to answer. Some possible questions are: "How else can I define this energy running through my body?" "What could be easier?" "What could be lighter, softer, freer, more open?" To exert effort while asking is counterproductive. Do not demand a change. Be easy in your asking. Ask as if you were a curious child full of wonder. Allow yourself to *not* know what the answer will be. A full cup accepts nothing new. So empty the cup of your assumptions. Be receptive to the infinite intelligence of Spirit. Do not *try* to create an answer for yourself. Allow an answer to *arise*.

Digging into your past patterns isn't compulsory. You don't have to discover the "why" of a situation. Becky, the girl who, as a child, lost her puppy doesn't necessarily need to immerse herself in years of therapy and "heal" her experiences of loss. All she has to do is use the *Mentastics Mantra* to unstick her labels, and ask, "What does this energy feel like?" "What is its shape, colour, and vibration?" "What other labels could be applied to it?" Then wait with innocence, with Beginner's Mind, for an answer to come. From this new perspective she is in a better position to offer forgiveness to the small child who was her former self.

The **forth step** is to *accept* Spirit's answer in accordance with your personal rhythm. Everyone has a personal rhythm, their sweet spot in which the pace of their life feels just right. Your rhythm depends on many factors: your age, where you live, your body's structure, how you hold yourself, your past stories, to name just a few.

Some people's personal rhythm is very fast most of the time; before they've even finished asking a question, Spirit gives them an answer. Others often have a much slower rhythm; their answer might come days after they've asked the question. Most have rhythms somewhere in between and all find that their sweet spot can vary from time to time depending on what else is happening in their life. Are they tired, sick, pre-occupied? With experience you'll get to know the pace at which your body / mind / Spirit operates. There is no sense fighting your rhythm. If you allow for it, it will be your most efficient and enjoyable ally.

Fast or slow or somewhere in between, you can rest assured if you ask a question of Spirit the way I've outlined, you *will* receive an answer. Depending on the nature of the question, the answer may not come in the way you expect, which is why you must stay with Beginner's Mind and release your assumptions. A response from Spirit can takes many forms: a split second flash of insight, a word that quietly appears in your mind, a conversation with a friend, a song, a line from a book, a TV show, a dream, etc. No matter where the answer comes from or what form it takes, it will resonate with you. You will know it.

Once you receive an answer, *trust* it. This is the **fifth step**.

Your answer comes from the infinite intelligence of the Unified Field. Your answer will lead you forward. And expand your horizons. But be wary of thinking this answer is the final one. Life unfolds. Your life is a process, not a destination. An answer generally leads to the next question, which leads you to the next answer, which leads to the next question, and so on ... all the way down the path of your personal evolution.

If you remember the encounter with my landlord, I took a few minutes, despite my seething anger, stepped off the sidewalk, used the *Mentastics Mantra* and got into *Presence*. With my assumptions lessened I asked a simple, open-ended question, "What other kind of labels could I apply to this energy?" Immediately, the words "power" and "aliveness" jumped to mind (which is unusual for me, because I generally have a slow personal rhythm.) This answer resonated deeply. I trusted it. I adopted it.

This is what you need to do, too. Trust. And adopt.

To recap, here are the steps to consciously ask a question and receive an answer of Spirit using the unconscious mind as a conduit.

1. Intend to address Spirit.

2. Using the *Mentastics Mantra*, enter a state of *Presence*.

3. Ask an open ended question.

4. Be attentive of your personal rhythm while awaiting an answer in *Presence*.

5. Trust the answer and adopt it.

Used all together, these five steps will simply, and with the least amount of suffering, allow you to change your interpretations of the energy running through your body/mind, as well as the old worn out stories you have attached to them. By remaining *present* and trusting the messages from Spirit—whether these messages come in the form of thoughts, pictures, feelings, conversations with other people, or bodily sensations—you will embark on the path of least resistance toward love and empowerment.

Making Decisions

Asking questions of Spirit has many more applications than re-labeling or changing the energetic patterns running through your body. This form of questioning can be used for all sorts of situations. It can help you make decisions for your highest good, whether the decisions to be made are mundane or profound. To navigate through life there is no better guide than Spirit.

As it stands, most of us are conditioned to automatically make decisions based on our past. Although this approach allows us to learn from our experiences, its downfall is that it recreates the past over and over again. It doesn't allow for anything new, for us to step outside of our box. We remain looped in the same old circuit.

Change is constant in the universe. We bump against the unknown on a daily (if not hourly) basis. In the midst of the unknown, allowing Spirit to lead the way is infinitely more advantageous than relying solely on past experiences.

So if you are at a crossroads, if you don't know what to choose or which way to go, ask Spirit by using the five steps I've outlined. Intend to address Spirit, get into *Presence*, make your query in an open-ended manner, be open and attentive in accordance with your rhythms, and then trust and adopt the answer that arises. By taking these steps consistently you will dramatically increase your certainty and allow into your life a seemingly magical intuition.

Practicing What I Preach

I have a writing partner who helps me craft the words and structure of my books. His name is Paul Latour and he is also my life partner. We have been together for more than a dozen years and, besides his gorgeous fair looks, I love and respect his creative and artistic abilities. Sometimes, however, his bullish Taurus nature can be overwhelming and controlling.

When I started this project, I wasn't sure how it was going to look. (I wanted it to be affordable and available worldwide. The Internet seemed to be the way to go.) I thought that a partnership with Paul might be a good idea since he was far more Internet savvy than I. We could contribute our unique skills to the project. I could add the content of my personal wisdom and experience. He could take my meandering writing style and add a linear structure so that those less familiar with the concepts could more easily understand.

Each day we sat side by side in his studio, with its red walls and long cedar table, to talk about how this project could manifest into a usable product. The farther into the project we got, the more I acquiesced to Paul's ideas over my own (an old pattern I thought I had totally released.) "Look,'" he would say, "if you want to enter the world of the Internet you need to learn how to market an idea. Check out how Bob Doyle, Jack Canfield, Bill Harris, Brendon Burchard and Bob Proctor flog their books."

So I explored the Internet to learn how to create a winning web design, how to link to other successful authors, how to create a compelling sales page and on and on.

Over time I found myself feeling increasingly despondent. I felt heavy, depressed, oppressed, unmotivated, low in energy, disinterested in life, and, well...fuzzy.

In my imagination I started to pick apart everything Paul did or said.

Finally, as we were deciding if the book should include free bonus gifts—a common theme with Internet gurus—I exploded. "I can't be like those guys!" I yelled. "I'm not a salesman and never want to be like that. I just have these wonderful tools I want the world to experience, and I have to present them in my own authentic way!"

The air sizzled in the aftermath of my eruption. We both pushed away from the cedar desk, got up, and left the room together.

"Okay," he said. "Let's practice what you preach. Let's pause a moment."

So, in unison we paused...and breathed. We felt our physical weight. Then we felt the imaginary weight of this project. In one hand we weighed the project as we had been going, the other hand weighed the idea of me taking the project back and sourcing out my weakest talents. We asked, "What could be lighter?"

I stayed *present*, I paused, breathed into my umbrella, felt the weight of my tail bone. I did it again and soon received an answer.

What felt lighter to me was taking on this project as my own and creating it using my own special skills. Paul could stay as a consultant but not an equal partner. When I explained my decision to Paul I felt light, uplifted, energized, bubbly, happy, open-hearted, playful and soft.

Paul's answer came a few days later while we were walking on the beach near our home. He shared that after he became *present* and weighed my decision on his own, nothing happened at first. Not until two days later did he get a response from Spirit in regards to this weighing. Suddenly when he thought about my E-book he felt a great weight had been lifted off his shoulders. He now was free to pursue his own creative projects and that made him feel energized and light.

I didn't force myself to feel better and neither did he. Such feelings came from our willingness to allow Spirit to lead the way while staying innocent in the *present moment*.

Rule of Thumb

The challenge with the five-step process is that it takes a few minutes (and sometimes a few days) to complete, so it's not always convenient.

In this day and age many of us are inundated with decisions we must make everyday. The sheer volume lends itself to automatic decision making. How we interact with co-workers, whether we have a donut or an apple with lunch, what clothes we wear, how we treat the waitress at dinner, whether to go with this or that supplier ... all of these decisions are often done so quickly we barely put any attention to them.

When you have time, use the five steps. They are the most thorough and effective way to make decisions and arrive at new solutions, both practical and creative. But when you lack time, a simple rule of thumb can often suffice.

As you practice the *Mentastics Mantra* and deepen your somatic experience of *Presence*, you will also increase your ability to notice the energetic patterns flowing through your body. This is a useful skill, because your emotions can help you make relatively quick decisions. We've all heard people say, "It just felt right," when talking about some decision they made. Well, that's what I'm talking about: making decisions that *feel* right, that follow Spirit.

Your ego-mind creates emotional patterns or vibrations that originate in fear, such as anxiety, lust, envy, control, heaviness, shame, apathy, etc. Your Spirit creates emotional patterns or vibrations that originate in love, such as acceptance, peace, play, joy, courageousness, lightness, passion, openness, etc. The rule of thumb is: *Make decisions that lean toward feelings rooted in love*.

So before you make a decision, take a few seconds, and pause. Breathe into your umbrella, feel the weight of some part of your body, and become attentive to what is actually happening *here* and *now*. Release the drama of your storyteller. Then consider your decision. With one choice in mind, notice the energy that runs through your body. Next notice the energy that runs through your body with the other choice in mind. Without attachment, observe the weight and character of each. Now make the choice that leans towards love. By doing this you will consistently follow the path of Spirit.

The point is to get in touch with how you *feel* about the situation, not whether some agenda is being filled. This does not mean that you will always choose the easy route. The most challenging path may very well be the one that gives you the feeling of lightness, joy, or play—a green light to go ahead and step onto that particular path.

With practice this will become second nature. Your emotions will become a valuable compass by which you can arrive at potent decisions in line with your highest good.

MENTASTICS EXERCISE: Making Decisions

(Also follow along with *Discerning the Origin of Your Emotions* track 5 on the audio download *Pathway to Presence*.)

This *Mentastics* Exercise will help you to discern the origin of your emotions, enabling you to make choices that are in line with your Spirit, your highest good.

Here is where your imagination can help you make the right decision.

1. *Get comfortable, you may want to sit or lie down for this exploration.*

2. *Close your eyes and take a couple of easy, deep breaths. Feel the weight of some part of your body, your pelvic girdle, your rib cage, or jaw. Pause...*

3. *Now, imagine making a choice between one thing and another. It can be an important choice or one as benign as going out to a movie or staying home to read a book. Just take what comes to you.*

4. *Imagine making one of these two choices (for example, going to see a movie). In your mind follow through with that choice (meeting your friend, paying your money, hearing the pre-movie advertising, tasting the popcorn....) Take your time with this. Allow your vision to innocently unfold.*

5. *The situation is now coming to an end. Give yourself permission to bring the sensations right into your body.*

6. *How do you feel? What label or labels would you use to describe the energy running through your body?*

7. *Now, put these emotions aside. Innocently ask yourself to remember them later.*

8. *Now shake your body out. That's right; get up and be like a swimmer warming up before a race. Gently shake those limbs; neutralise that biochemistry.*

9.   *Good. Now take a moment and pause. Breathe into your umbrella. Feel the weight of some part of your body. Pause...*

10.   *Your next step is to imagine the alternate choice. Put yourself into the situation and allow it to unfold.*

11.   *Get into it. Don't assume what it will be like.*

12.   *The situation is now coming to an end. Give yourself permission to bring the sensation right into your body.*

13.   *How do you feel? How would you describe the energy running through your body?*

14.   *Okay. Do the swimmer warm-up thing again. Gently shake your limbs.*

15.   *Take a deep umbrella breath. Pause...*

16.   *Now, ask yourself to recall the emotion generated by each scenario. Imagine one as a ball of energy in your left hand and the other as a ball of energy in your right hand.*

17.   *Feel the weight of each.*

18.   *Which feels most like lightness, like bliss, like peace?*

Congratulations! You've just discerned the choice originating from Spirit, in line with your highest good. Try this the next time you have to make a decision. You'll be amazed by the clarity it creates.

Little Moments

Consider that, after applying for several jobs, you receive offers on the two you want most. Both jobs offer the same amount of money and benefits and both are in a location you prefer. All the information you have gathered says both are very promising. How can you decide which one to accept? Sit back in your chair, close your eyes and pause…take a deep umbrella breath and feel the weight of some part of your body. Give yourself permission to imagine the first offer. Imagine yourself walking into the office, talking to your co-workers, working together on an important project. Notice how it feels in your body while in that imaginary experience.

Great. Now put this aside to be recalled later.

Next imagine the second job. Go through the same scenario: pause, take a deep umbrella breath, and feel the weight of some part of your body. Imagine walking into the office, talking to these co-workers, working on a project together.

Notice how this scene feels.

Now, bring this imagining to a close.

Like in the previous exercise, pause, breathe, and feel the weight of the first scenario in your left hand and the weight of the second scenario in your right hand. Which feels lighter? More open? Offers an overall feeling of rightness?

Consider shopping for that perfect outfit to celebrate your anniversary. Two dresses stand out from all the rest. Which one to buy?

There is little time to decide as the store is about to close, so use the rule of thumb. Close your eyes, pause for a moment. Let go of any preconceived ideas you may have. Be unconcerned if your life partner likes it, what others think about it, how you think you look in the mirror. Breathe into your umbrella. Say "Hi there," to your tailbone. Feel the over-all "weight" of wearing one outfit. (And I'm not talking about how much the material weighs!) Notice your reaction.

Next, do the same with the other outfit. Pause, breathe, release, and feel the over-all "weight" of wearing the other outfit.

Which outfit gives you smiles, a feeling of openness, and a "Yes??"

One decision at a time *can* transform your life.

By practicing *Presence* and aligning yourself with Spirit, not only will you loosen your attachments and perceive things more accurately, the growth of your life will naturally inch towards the lightness of love.

Building a life is a cumulative process. It is a path. The simple and profound tools I have shown you are the footsteps you can take, one after another, to lead you forward. Take them. They are your birthright and your gift to the world.

CHAPTER SEVEN

Releasing Holding Patterns

Daniel and David, the impish freckled five-year-old twins who had their theatrical debut in *Green Cheese Pie*, have since grown up. Their hair is no longer a mop but a brush cut of coppery bristles. During adolescence their freckles faded and now only appear when embarrassed. David has followed in his father's footsteps and embarked on an architectural degree at the University of BC, while Daniel enrolled in a physiotherapy program in Toronto. At the end of their third post-secondary year, they return home to Victoria, BC. Their planes land within five minutes of each other. When they arrive at the terminal they look for their Dad, who is supposed to pick them up, but find only each other.

"Danny-boy," exclaims David.

Daniel knows who it is before he sees him. No one else calls him by that name. Daniel turns to face his mirror-like image. "Davie-boy," he says as they hug.

Then David grasps Daniel firmly by the shoulders. "Have you gotten over that cold little brother?" he asks with a mild shake.

"Yeah, I'm finally over it. Darn thing always hits me in the chest and throat."

"Always the sickly one," David comments.

Daniel looks at the gathering crowd in the baggage claim area. The carousel hasn't yet started. "So," he says, "how's the family's newest architectural genius?"

"I'm—um," David glances away, looking first to the baggage area, and then back to Daniel. To change the subject he cocks his head and gives Daniel one of his patented impish grins. "Is it just me, or have you gotten shorter? Then again, maybe it's me that's gotten taller?"

"We're the same height we've always been," Daniel sighs.

"No really," says David. "You *do* look shorter. It's your posture, bro. All that physiotherapy training and you still can't stand up straight."

Daniel catches on to his brother's aversion tactics. "So, school's not going so well?"

David, the master of avoidance, looks around for their father. "Let's grab a brew while we wait."

In the airport lounge they order a couple of pints. David takes a long pull and then smiles, a line of foam on his upper lip.

"What's up?" asks Daniel.

David glances out the window, looking again for their father's black Volvo. "I've dropped out," he admits.

"You're kidding me?"

"I never wanted to be an architect anyway. That was Dad's dream."

"But you've only got a year left."

"Actually, I dropped out in January."

Now it's Daniel's turn to look out the window for the black Volvo. "What have you been doing all year?" he says. "What did you do with the tuition money?

"I've been taking acting classes."

"Does Dad know?"

"I love acting, bro."

"Are you crazy?"

"Listen to me," says David, "I know it sounds cliché, but acting is my passion. It's what I'm here to do."

Daniel shakes his head. David has always been the flamboyant one, never afraid to get up in front of a crowd. "I just can't relate," says Daniel. "It scares the 'bejesus' out of me just to get up in front of my ten classmates, never mind a big audience"

"You'd think as twins we'd be more alike."

"You'd think. But when I even picture the spotlight, my chest and throat clam up." Daniel forms a fist in front of his chest to illustrate. "My heart beats triple time. I become paralyzed. I want to throw up!"

"I feel the same way," David says with real enthusiasm, picturing the stage in his mind. "My chest and throat tighten right up, too. My heart starts to pound and it's like someone's amped up the electricity. That's when I know I'm ready to rock! Do you remember *Green Cheese Pie*?"

"Yeah."

"Well, Mom told me something I'll never forget. Before I went backstage I confessed I was—you know—a little nervous. She told me I wasn't *actually* nervous; that the opposite was in fact true. This feeling meant I would do my best. And she was right. If I don't have that feeling before a performance, *that's* when I get really nervous."

Just then a pair of hands thump down on the opposite side of the table. The twins turn. It's their father. "Is there room at this party for one more?"

Later, sitting on his lumpy single mattress in his childhood bedroom, Daniel remembers what his father said to him on the *Green Cheese Pie* day. "You must be scared. I would be. Don't worry though." This, of course, only made Daniel worry all the more. After all, if his big and successful father would be scared, who was Daniel to be anything else? Could it be that after *Green Cheese Pie* Daniel assumed that being on display equaled stress?

Daniel can't actually remember all the times his chest and throat tightened, his heart rate accelerated and his stomach did back flips, but his intuition tells him it was regular and often: girls, dances, reading out loud in front of class, playing basketball, receiving his diploma...

He contemplates an idea. What if his father had told him the same thing that his mother told David? Would he relate to the spotlight differently? Would he have walked a different road in this regard? Would he be more assertive and confident? Could he have gotten the girl? Played better sports? Danced to his heart's content? Could his father's words have been the domino that sent his life in a very different direction than his brother's? Or was it just Karma, life paying him back? Or, perhaps destiny!!!

As an experiment he enrolls in a summer acting class with his brother David. But despite adopting his brother's labels, despite his visualizations, his studying, and his practice sessions, Daniel becomes constantly overwhelmed by his sick stomach, tight chest, racing heart, and clammed-up throat. He feels physically incapable. His voice gets squeaky, his hands become shaky, and his thoughts become incoherent. He hates it. After two weeks he drops out.

Although Daniel suspected his pattern of behavior was rooted in his theatrical debut experience, he couldn't translate that knowledge into a new way of being. His conscious decision wasn't strong enough to make a lasting difference. Why? Was it destiny after all?

The leap that Daniel did not make was the physical nature of his old belief. After his first traumatic *Green Cheese Pie* experience, he had felt and thought up variations on the same theme for so long that they had transmuted his physical being as well. His slightly hunched posture and his propensity for chest colds and throat infections indicated a distinct tension in the muscles of his chest and throat that were a reflection of his beliefs. For Daniel these symptoms were outside his control. In fact, he had become so accustomed to them that they no longer registered, being utterly unconscious. So when he tried to take different actions and change his results, he bumped against the unyielding effects of these physical "holdings," which automatically created conditions in his body—sick stomach, tight chest, racing heart, and clammed up throat—overwhelming his mind.

Part of Daniel's challenge was his approach, an approach many of us take. He, like many of us, believed conscious action and effort would suffice in getting the results he wanted. But, because his body didn't co-operate, he needed to delve into his unconscious and shine a light on the dysfunctional beliefs. This didn't mean he had to dredge up *all* his thoughts around stage fright, or spend thousands of dollars on analysis. Daniel only needed to *feel* what it would be like *without* this pattern. That would have given him the frame of reference he needed.

Intimate Connections

The mind and the body are intimately connected. Even though Daniel discovered that his stage fright was self-created, he became aware only of the mind component. He didn't take into account that the mind and body are interconnected. He would have to address both components of his stage fright—the mind and the body—in order to foster lasting change.

The mind and body reflect and reinforce each other. Pain, tension, and stress in the body are often the result of resonant thoughts and feelings habitually re-run in the mind. And once the "holding patterns" are in place in the body they reinforce the "holding patterns" in the mind; one feeding on the other—back and forth, back and forth.

If your inner storyteller tells a happy story (and you *believe* it) you will feel happiness. Your body will reflect this. Your muscles will relax. Your posture will lift. You'll have a smile on your face and spring in your step. You don't have to *make* this happen. You don't have to direct your body to do this. It's automatic. Conversely, if your storyteller tells you a sad story, (and you *believe* it) you experience repercussions in the body. Your chest will cave in, your shoulders will slump, your eyes and chin will drop. Again, this is automatic.

Such repercussions don't work just in the direction from thoughts to feelings to physical manifestation. They work the other way around, too. If your body takes on peaceful, delightful movements—chest held high, a smile on your face, lightness to your step—then your storyteller tends to start telling lighter, happier stories.

Habitual or chronic thoughts become set in the unconscious and the feelings are translated into a holding pattern in the body, where the energy is literally "held" in place. For example, Daniel's stage fright was "held" in place by the tense muscles in his stomach, chest and throat, just as Becky's shame and guilt were "held" in place by the tension in her torso and the fat buffer around her body.

This is where things get *really* sticky. Such psychophysical translation occurs in our posture, our biochemistry, and in the condition of our muscles, joints, tendons, organs, etc. The body becomes conditioned to be a certain way. In time, you no longer make a choice. It is utterly unconscious.

The question is: How can you shift a debilitating holding pattern once it has become set in the body?

People rarely think of their slumped shoulders and tight backs as a reflection of their consistent inner way of being. People hardly ever consider that their painful knees have anything to do with the stories of instability constantly running through their heads. Most believe chronic throat infections are isolated occurrences that have little in common with stifled self-expression. Even if they are aware of a connection, they seldom know how to undo it. They are held in the grips of such "holding patterns."

If noticing your breath and weight has a stickiness factor of 2 out of 10, and your emotions are 11 out of 10, then holding patterns in the body are a 15!

There is no doubt that psychophysical holding patterns are a huge challenge. They can manifest in all sorts of ways: body pain, depression, anxiety, and procrastination, to name only a few. They not only cause us pain, they keep us circling the same old loops.

Presence and Release

Dr Trager said on multiple occasions that all he really had to offer was *Hook-Up*. I believe that part of his motivation for repeating this is because he knew the power of the *Now*. He knew the act of bringing yourself into *Presence* will, all by itself, help release psychophysical holding patterns.

Imagine the body/mind as a large pipe or conduit that over the years has been clogged with the mud and debris of life, including all our pains and limitations, all of our past stories and future expectations. Using the *Mentastics Mantra* to connect to the *present moment* is akin to opening a valve that sends pure clean water (the flow of Spirit, of the Life Force) through our pipe. Each time this pure energy courses through, a little more of the muck is cleaned out.

As your pipe clears, this clarity is reflected in your body and therefore your mind. This is yet another reason why it is so important to keep coming back to the *Mantra*, to the *present moment*. It is our natural state to be free and clear. If we trust and allow, this will happen automatically.

Sessions and Release

There is a reason the *Trager* Approach is also called *Trager Psychophysical Integration*. Using the principles of this approach is an excellent and gentle way for anyone to explore new possibilities. A session brings together presence, awareness, and a tactile invitation to adopt new possible ways of being for the body's holding patterns.

A *Trager* session uses gentle, non-intrusive touch and physical movement to invite the body/mind of the person on the table to experience feelings of lightness, of softness, of bliss through *Hook-Up*.

"[A session] involves the transmission of feeling messages from my unconscious mind to their unconscious mind."
Milton Trager [6]

If you were to have a *Trager* session, you would find that no oils or lotions are used. You would lie passively on a well-padded table (clothed or partially unclothed, as you choose) while the practitioner, who is consciously in *Hook-Up*, gently rocks, compresses, elongates, jiggles, and shimmers the tissue in your body. You would experience the practitioner playing along the border of restriction and freedom, inviting into your tissue the ever-so-wonderful feelings of lightness, softness, and bliss.

This session would soon become a movement re-education that addressed the physical and non-physical aspects of your body/mind, thereby giving you (whether you were aware of it or not) an alternative to any limited physical and mental patterns you might be holding on to. Through the deep, but nonintrusive touch, your practitioner would introduce you to the place of all possibility, to the origin of everything that you have ever thought, felt, or imagined, to that life-giving, life-regulating power all around us. You would know this by the expansive open feeling in your tissue, as if the gravity holding you down had lessened. You would know this by how your joints would seem to have been lubricated, how your breath would deepen, how your mind would quiet. The combination of the practitioner's skill at the craft plus their ability to be in the *present moment* (and thereby *Hook-Up* to Source) allows for such transference.

[7]

If you have not had a *Trager* session I encourage you to seek out a practitioner and make an appointment. It is truly a profound and wonderful experience that can make a significant difference to the release of old unwanted psychophysical holding patterns.

Questioning and Release

The tools I've outlined in this book can help you accelerate the natural clearing of your body/mind and support the unwinding created through sessions. If you choose, you can consciously promote the release of debilitating holding patterns. You can foster change in your posture, your biochemistry, and the condition of your muscles, joints, and organs—a change that mirrors Spirit—with feelings of empowerment, ease, grace, and lightness.

However, the physicality of holding patterns sometimes results in a lag time that can be demoralizing. It's like losing weight. Picturing yourself as thin and energetic, and feeling yourself as fit and full of life are crucial steps, but there is no getting away from the time it takes to shed the pounds. Releasing holding patterns is most often (but not always) a step-by-step process that takes longer than re-labeling or shifting an emotional pattern. It's important to acknowledge this possibility before you start.

The process of releasing your psychophysical holding patterns starts by becoming attentive to your body. It is a direct reflection of your unconscious mind. You may not be able to be aware of your unconscious, but you can be aware of your body and, through it, communicate with your unconscious as well as with Spirit.

First use the *Mentastics Mantra*. Pause and release your expectations. Pause again and let go of what you *think* you are "holding." Breathe into your umbrella. Feel the weight of some part of your body. Pause again. Breathe. Feel weight. Release expectations. Release meaning. Now scan your body. Is there an area that feels tight, painful, or uncomfortable? If there is, put your attention there. If there is not, scan your body again. Is there an area that you can't feel? An area in which you don't perceive energy or feeling? If there is, place your attention there.

Explore either area with your awareness.

Don't try to make it better or different. Don't try to make it do anything. Don't bring an agenda to the table. It's not about action or effort. Allow it to be as it is. Be innocent.

The unconscious wants to work for you. It wants to give you what you want, but it does not respond well to effort. Dr. Trager taught that effort keeps things in place. "Get over trying," he said, "trying is effort and effort brings tension. *Allow* it to come forward." Fighting against a holding pattern, being frustrated with it, keeps it in place. Inner battles always result in inner loss. When you exert effort to change some inner dynamic you are in fact reinforcing the element you wish to change. Daniel's failure to overcome his stage fright was in part due to the fact that he fought against himself.

Before long, what he battled got stronger. What you resist persists. So use Beginner's Mind. Simply notice what's going on. Notice what emotions may or may not be present. Notice what physical sensations are there.

"Hook-Up is not a passive state. It is dynamic, alive, vibrant; yet peaceful. There isn't anything one has to do to Hook-Up except to allow it to happen. Even learning and trying to let go is an effort. There is no effort. There is no design."

Milton Trager [8]

If you find yourself bringing an agenda to the table or losing focus, simply and without drama go back to the *Mantra*. Then with Beginner's Mind return your awareness to the area.

When you are ready, you can communicate with your unconscious through your holding pattern by asking an open-ended question. Again do not demand a change. Be easy in your asking. You could ask, "What other label could I use?" "What could be easier?" "What could be lighter?" "How can I be more open?" Whatever the question, allow yourself to *not* know what the answer will be. Creating an answer for yourself is counterproductive. Instead allow an answer to *arise*.

The answer can be a word or a thought or a picture. But often it is a physical emotional release. What's released depends on what was being held. For example, if what's being held is the result of sexual trauma, the release might be tears and screams and strong movement followed by a sense of safety and liberation. If what's being held is stage fright, the release might feel like a jubilant sense of openness as if you've grown taller, straighter, and more confident. If the holding is due to repetitive motion from too much work, the release might be a deep sense of softness and relief. No matter what the answer is—an understanding or a physical release—it is a good thing. Trust it. Follow it. You are in the process of releasing a clog or an impediment in the pipe of your body/mind.

Be courageous in the face of any release. It's best to expect and welcome them. They are an adjustment in your body and mind that allows more love and peace into your life. Sometimes holding patterns let go all at once. Sometimes they let go gradually over time. Either way, they are crucial steps on the path to becoming your authentic self. Without these releases, without this process of questioning and response, your body/mind will stay clogged with your past traumas and conditioning. Step out of victimhood. Step into empowerment. Don't expect life to change if you don't change something in your life.

MENTASTICS EXERCISE:

Regulating the Release of a Holding Pattern

(Also follow along with *Regulating the Release of a Holding Pattern* track 6 on the audio download *Pathway to Presence*.)

1. *Find a comfortable position in which you can easily explore your body through movement. You can be standing or sitting (or, if you need to, lying down.)*

2. *Now, take some easy, deep, leisurely breaths and when you exhale, allow your mind to settle.*

3. *Continue this easy, deep breathing and allow the stillness to deepen. As you breathe in and out, feel your torso as an umbrella opening and closing with ease.*

4. *Imagine a sky hook connecting your crown to the cosmic energies gently pulling you skyward.*

5. *Bring your awareness to your spinal column. Follow it down, down to your tail bone where an imaginary tail grows and grows until it is long enough to trail on the ground. Feel the tripod-like stability it brings.*

6. *Wiggle your toes and bring your awareness to where your feet connect with the earth.*

7. *Slowly shift your weight from side to side noticing, without judgement, how your body moves. As you shift, be an innocent explorer. Become aware of your body's aliveness, of the e-motion flowing through it.*

8. *Now, as you continue to gently shift your weight, recall a situation that caused you some distress, emotionally or physically. It doesn't matter if it is old or recent, big or small. Just take what comes to you. As best you can put yourself into the situation. Where are you? What are you doing? Are other people there? What is being said?*

What is your response? Take your time. Be courageous. Feel what you feel.

9. *Now, softly scan your body. Do you notice any restriction, heaviness, or pain? Where in your body do you feel this? Be with this holding pattern. There is no need to push against it or run away from it. Simply say, "Hi there!"*

10. *Explore how this holding pattern feels. If it had a shape, what would it be? If it had texture, a smell, or a colour, what would they be? How much does it weigh?*

11. *As you continue to shift your weight from side to side, innocently ask that area, "What could feel lighter?" You are not trying to make it light, you are simply curious.*

12. *Now, pause... your movement. Breathe into your umbrella, feel your sky hook, your tail and the bottoms of your feet. Notice the area where you put your attention. Is there a change?*

13. *Once more shift your weight from side to side, side to side. Feel your sky hook, your feet, your tail, your umbrella, and ask without expectation, "What could be lighter than that?"*

14. *Alright, pause your movement again. Notice the area. How is it this time?... Start your weight shifting once more; connect your sky hook, breathe into your umbrella, and feel the bottoms of your feet, your tail dusting the floor behind you. Feel all of this.*

15. *Now, ask the same spot, "How can this lightness go deeper inside?" Remember you have no agenda, you are simply curious waiting with innocence for an answer.*

16. *Pause yet again. Notice. How does the area feel now? Has its weight changed? Its colour, texture or smell? Has its shape altered? What changes can you discern?*

If you want, you can continue the process of questioning until you experience some release, making sure you pause often to notice any change. When you are finished, breathe into this newly transformed area. Allow it to incorporate into your body, mind and Spirit. Later when you experiment on your own, you can ask of your holding patterns other questions like, "What could be softer? Freer? Safer? More open? More peaceful? More flexible?" Or whatever open-ended questions that feel intuitively right for you.

Smoothing Out the Process

I would love to tell you that the process of releasing old holding patterns—stiff backs, tight shoulders, hard bellies, and chronic headaches—is always wonderful and blissful, but unfortunately I cannot. Sometimes the shift is gentle, and sometimes it's downright uncomfortable.

To smooth out the process of release, use the *Mentastics Mantra*. Pause, breath mindfully into your imaginary umbrella, and feel the weight in your body as you move through space. Then, with Beginner's Mind, simply notice the energy and sensations. Let go of the old stories you've attached to your holding. Be with how it is. Accept it. It's merely energy moving out of your body/mind. Only by attaching yourself to the associated stories will you perpetuate your suffering.

I promise you that as the process unfolds you *will* feel lighter and more expansive, and you *will* automatically move toward more empowerment and a fuller, richer life. In other words, it's worth it. I've seen it time and again. I've experienced it for myself.

Remember, this is a cumulative process. The more you practice, the easier it becomes, transforming both your inner and outer life.

CHAPTER EIGHT

Trager Is...

Trager is an experience. All the words you have read are only a means to an end. The end is an experience. Intellectual concepts don't hold a candle to the real thing. Life is not only lived in our heads; it's also lived in our bodies. In experience.

> *"Not until we experience it is it more than just words.*
> *After we experience it there is no need for words. The*
> *value of words is to stimulate the desire to experience."*
>
> Milton Trager [9]

Trager is about *Hook-Up*, a hooking up to the ever-present *Now*. This connection is personal and intimate. It is a conscious connection to Source, to Spirit, to the intelligent Life Force that always has been and always will be all around us. This is the experience Dr. Milton

Trager wanted to impart. He created *Mentastics* so that anyone could have this experience, not only while meditating, but while working, while relating to others, while typing on the computer, writing a book, moving a client's limbs, driving a car, walking down the road, sitting on the beach—every facet of life.

"Hook-Up is the same as meditation. And like meditation, there are many levels. One can go deeper and deeper into a state that is beyond relaxation. A step beyond relaxation is Peace."

Milton Trager [10]

Trager is about simplicity, the simplicity of three tools—the *Mentastics Mantra*—that can unstick you from the attachments to your stories and e-motional labels. With reduced attachment you see the world and yourself more accurately. With a deepened sense of *Presence* you are able to make new choices, fresh choices, choices beyond past paradigms, aligned with your highest good. Through practice you will emit deep peace and empowerment.

"When you really experience Hook-Up your projection of peace to everyone around you will be such that they will be influenced and respond to your vibrations... People will want to be around you, or help you out more simply because your projection of joy and ease will be contagious."

Milton Trager [11]

Trager is about ease. Effort is its antithesis. When something is hard, go lighter. Trying creates stress that reinforces old patterns. Using your force of will to push, to obsess, to work too hard, only creates an opposite reaction. Instead, simply notice what is going on. Say "Hi there." Stay out of the way of the intelligent Life Force. Release your stories and expectations. Feel your body.

> *"Do not try. To try is an effort, and effort creates tension... Consciously stay out of it... When you feel tightness and stiffness in your body do not attack it and do not try to make it freer, which is the natural reaction for the majority of people."*
>
> Milton Trager [12]

Trager is about speaking with your unconscious through the holding patterns in the body. Your unconscious mind is connected to and expressed through the body. You can elicit a new way of being through this connection. This can be done on a table with a practitioner present and/or on your own with *Mentastics*.

> *"What keeps the body restricted is not a true physical block, but a mental pattern block. It is the mind that unconsciously directs the function of the body. The block exists in the mind."*
>
> Milton Trager [13]

91

Hook up into a state of *Presence.* Ask an open-ended question. Stay innocently receptive with Beginner's Mind, without assumptions. You will receive an answer or series of evolving answers that peel away the layers of your holding.

> *"Ask the questions in a soft, undemanding manner in which you expect the answer to come."*
>
> Milton Trager [14]

Trager is about releasing old patterns lodged in your body/mind and replacing them with new, more pleasurable experiences. Though your unconscious mind never forgets, it will always adopt, if given the choice, a more gratifying alternative. So be courageous. Bring keen awareness to your pain. Accept it with softness. Don't *try* to get rid of it. Instead, ask for a better option.

> *"Play with the tension or pain you feel. Do not try to get rid of it. The tighter or more painful the area is, the softer you must become."*
>
> Milton Trager [15]

> *"When the tension and blocks are released, one experiences more energy and a greater sense of aliveness."*
>
> Milton Trager [16]

Trager is a powerful and personal approach to getting through the tough times of life. The lessons in this book really shine as coping tools for the body and the mind. Quiet the storyteller in your head with short or long pauses. Practice umbrella breathing. Feel the weight of your body while in motion. Used in concert, these tools will open you to a sense of aliveness. In this aliveness you can—even in the midst of grief or anger or pain—feel peace.

> *"Mentastics have helped me so much and are such an integral part of my life, that I do them automatically whenever I am walking, getting up out of a chair, or reaching for a glass off the shelf."*
>
> Milton Trager [17]

Trager is about mastery and practice. It is a path to living that unfolds with intelligence every moment of every day. It doesn't matter who you are or where you come from. Your background, your physical condition, your spiritual orientation are all irrelevant. You need only step onto the path. Your reward will be an ever-deepening *experience* of *Trager*, of *Hook-Up*, of a conscious connection to the beauty in and of the world.

> *"[Mentastics] is an art; and like any other art, practice can bring about beauty and form."*
>
> Milton Trager [18]

Trager is an approach. It is not dogma or a strict code of actions. The tools I have outlined in this book can be employed in any order that feels intuitively right to you in any moment. They are an organic process. They combine and flow into one another. Together they form a perpetual circle that promotes a moment-to-moment, body-centered awareness.

You don't have to start with a pause. Your mind may be spinning, belting out story after story, unwilling to be still. If this happens—and it is bound to—don't *try* to turn down the volume. Don't fight your storyteller or suppress her story. Simply and gently turn your attention: breathe into your umbrella or feel the weight of your rib cage moving in and out. Shift your body from side to side, feeling the wave of motion down your backbone. Feel the weight of your hands as you softly bounced them up and down. Or, go for a walk. Feel your arms swinging, your pelvic girdle shifting as you put one foot in front of the other. Feel the soles of your feet making contact with the ground, your toes rolling off your heels like having rocking-chair-feet.

You have nothing to do, nothing to control. You are not required to have a plan. There is no need to push. Simply be aware. Pay attention. Be innocently curious. That's all!

"As you are doing the movements, you may think, "It can't be this easy. I am barely doing anything physically. And yet, I feel a change has occurred." It is a personal, intimate experience. It is a happening of the moment."

Milton Trager [19]

Forcing yourself to employ these concepts is counter-productive. Instead, play with them. Experiment with them. You'll find them to be flexible and interconnected. With practice you'll also find yourself able to use more than one simultaneously. Just do what is right for you. Soon your unconscious mind will be reminding you to pause, or breathe into your umbrella, or feel the weight of some part of your body. It will ask:

"Could we have a pause here?"

"Could this be easier?"

CHAPTER NINE

The Results

No matter the order which you use the *Mentastics* in this book, there will be two consistent results.

The first is *Hook-Up*, an ever growing conscious awareness of the flow of the life-regulating, life-giving force that is everywhere; a force that, when you become comfortable with its flow, feels like delicious, scrumptious, unconditional, unbounded, open-ended, and infinite love. (Oh yeah!)

The second result is *Presence*. By using these simple *Mentastics* you will start to live your life differently. You will live in *Presence*. By *Presence* I mean being consistently aware of yourself as a spiritual being who is having a physical experience.

No longer will you tend to become overwhelmed and distracted by your thoughts and stories, by your fears and worries, anxieties and stresses. No longer will your mind be spinning and fretting about what you perceive as the future, or what your memory tells you of the past. You will have arrived consciously and somatically into the vibrancy of the *Here* and *Now*.

Of course, *Pathway to Presence* is only a first step, a gateway to the path of designing your life and learning how to live in *Presence* on a consistent basis while moving through a world that is rife with paradox.

Life is complex—there's no getting around that. But *Presence* can be simple, direct, somatic, and blissful. Despite trials and tribulations, you can still have an underlying sense of peace and aliveness. This is accomplished through *Presence*, through *Hook-Up*, fostered by the consistent use of *Mentastics*.

Only through experience, only by *feeling* what I am talking about in both your body and mind will you really live it.

Good Journey!

Appendix

Trager International

[1] The *Trager* Institute came into being in 1976 shortly after Dr. Trager gave a demonstration of his abilities at California's famed Esalen Institute in Big Sur. Afterward, Betty Fuller, a class coordinator at Big Sur, followed Milton Trager for a month to learn more about this unique approach to body/mind integration. She was one of the initial developers and soon became the first director of the newly formed *Trager* Institute.

In the year 2000 the structure and name changed to *Trager* International to give more autonomy to national organizations.

Currently there are national organizations in multiple countries, with yearly national general meetings, and a large international conference about every four years. Go to www.Trager.com to find a practitioner in your country.

A Few Notes on the Professional Training

A *Trager* practitioner candidate undergoes intensive training, requiring supervised training hours plus field work and tutorials (exact hours depend on the laws of each country).

A Certified *Trager* Practitioner's education does not stop at certification, however. Continuing education is required because learning to be a beginner is highly valued, as is putting ones work in question. One form of questioning built into the curriculum includes tutorials with a certified Tutor. Tutors act as the regional liaisons to the international body and serve to continuously broaden a practitioner's knowledge, as well as deepen their effectiveness on a client's body.

Personal experience has taught me that a student undergoes much inner growth before and after certification. As *presence* is anchored into the practice, the training and work is often experienced as a spiritual path.

To learn more about the Professional *Trager* Training go to www.Trager.com.

Acknowledgments

I would like to acknowledge those who have helped me bring *Pathway to Presence*, the e-Book and CD combo to fruition.

First and foremost, my life (and writing) partner, Paul Latour. Without his creative talents and endless patience this book would not have gotten off the ground.

To Jill Kirby and Susan Healey for taking the time out of their busy lives to proofread the end copy, bringing the quality of the e-Book up a notch or two.

To Jean Hopkins, traveling *Trager* Instructor extraordinaire, who helped clean up my act, both in my sessions and e-Book.

To Jake Galbraith for a fine recording of the CD.

To Denis Donnelly for contributing his beautiful harp music on the CD. To hear more go to www.denisdonnelly.ca .

Endnotes

---

[1] Book Epigraph: Bhagavad Gita, Chapter 6, verse 5

Chapter 1: The Path

[2] Australian Institute of Health and Welfare, 1998. "National Health Priority Areas Mental Health: A Report Focusing on Depression." Depression statistics in Australia are comparable to those of the US and UK.

[3] NIMH. "The Numbers Count: Mental Illness in America," "www.nimh.nih.gov/publicat/numbers.cfm" \t "_blank" <u>Science on Our Minds Fact Sheet Series</u>

[4] Study published in *Psychiatric Services*, April 2004. Reported in our health news archive: "www.upliftprogram.com/ h_depression.html" \l "h77" <u>Pill-Popping Pre-Schoolers,</u>

"www.upliftprogram.com/h_depression.html" \l "h80" <u>Even Toddlers Get the Blues</u>

Chapter 2: The Fundamental Element

[5] Milton Trager in *Trager Mentastics: Movement as a Way to Agelessness* by Milton Trager, MD with Cathy Hammond, Ph.D. (Barrytown, NY: Station Hill, 1987), P.77

Chapter 7: Releasing Holding Patterns: Session and Release

[6] Milton Trager in *Trager Mentastics: Movement as a Way to Agelessness* by Milton Trager, MD with Cathy Hammond, Ph.D. (Barrytown, NY: Station Hill, 1987), P.98

[7] Taken from *Trager for Self-Healing: A Practical Guide for Living in the Present Moment* by Audrey Mairi (Tiburon and Novato CA: HJ Kramer/New World Library, 2006), P.6

[8] Milton Trager in *Trager Mentastics: Movement as a Way to Agelessness* by Milton Trager, MD with Cathy Hammond, Ph.D. (Barrytown, NY: Station Hill, 1987), P.59

Chapter 8: Trager Is...

[9] Milton Trager, unpublished class teachings, San Diego, 1979

[10] Milton Trager in *Trager Mentastics: Movement as a Way to Agelessness* by Milton Trager, MD with Cathy Hammond, Ph.D. (Barrytown, NY: Station Hill, 1987), P.57

[11] Milton Trager in *Trager Mentastics: Movement as a Way to Agelessness* by Milton Trager, MD with Cathy Hammond, Ph.D. (Barrytown, NY: Station Hill, 1987), P.99

[12] Milton Trager in *Trager Mentastics: Movement as a Way to Agelessness* by Milton Trager, MD with Cathy Hammond, Ph.D. (Barrytown, NY: Station Hill, 1987), P.44 & 45

[13] Milton Trager in *Trager Mentastics: Movement as a Way to Agelessness* by Milton Trager, MD with Cathy Hammond, Ph.D. (Barrytown, NY: Station Hill, 1987), P.40

[14] Milton Trager in *Trager Mentastics: Movement as a Way to Agelessness* by Milton Trager, MD with Cathy Hammond, Ph.D. (Barrytown, NY: Station Hill, 1987), P.47

[15] Milton Trager in *Trager Mentastics: Movement as a Way to Agelessness* by Milton Trager, MD with Cathy Hammond, Ph.D. (Barrytown, NY: Station Hill, 1987), P.93

[16] Milton Trager in *Trager Mentastics: Movement as a Way to Agelessness* by Milton Trager, MD with Cathy Hammond, Ph.D. (Barrytown, NY: Station Hill, 1987), P.83

[17] Milton Trager in *Trager Mentastics: Movement as a Way to Agelessness* by Milton Trager, MD with Cathy Hammond, Ph.D. (Barrytown, NY: Station Hill, 1987), P.110

[18] Milton Trager in *Trager Mentastics: Movement as a Way to Agelessness* by Milton Trager, MD with Cathy Hammond, Ph.D. (Barrytown, NY: Station Hill, 1987), P.54

[19] Milton Trager in *Trager Mentastics: Movement as a Way to Agelessness* by Milton Trager, MD with Cathy Hammond, Ph.D. (Barrytown, NY: Station Hill, 1987), P.52

About the Author

Audrey Mairi is a Trager practitioner, tutor, teacher, and Reiki Master. She regularly holds workshops for students and therapists, dealing with the connection of body, mind, and Spirit.

In her teenage years she became curious of the mind/Spirit aspect of the trinity, which prompted her to start studying Transcendental Meditation in 1969 (first in Canada and later in Vittel France). By 1976 she was an associate teacher of TM®.

Later her interests grew to include the body aspect of the trinity which led her to immunology research at Queens University/Kingston General Hospital. This, in turn, intensified her thirst to know more about energy medicine, which prompted her to become a Reiki Master and explore Shamanic light body exercises, Shamanic drumming, Soul Recovery, and Holotropic Breath-work.

This life long exploration culminated in her certification as a *Trager* Psychophysical Integration practitioner in 1985, and continued to escalate when she became a *Trager* tutor in 1993, and then an electives teacher in 2003. She served as Canada's representative on the Trager Tutor Committee and as a member of the transitional board of directors of Trager International.

As a Spiritual seeker, Audrey has travelled through Europe, North Africa, and the United States, studying the intricate interweaving of body, mind, and Spirit.

Audrey lives—and sings with the Gettin' Higher Choir—in beautiful Victoria, British Columbia.

To book or attend a workshop by Audrey Mairi, visit her website at www.audreymairi.com .

Made in the USA
Middletown, DE
13 April 2016